This World
of Living Things

By

PAUL GRISWOLD HOWES

Curator of the Bruce Museum of Natural History
History and Art
Greenwich, Connecticut

With Illustrations by the Author

DUELL, SLOAN AND PEARCE
New York

This World
of Living Things

Books by

PAUL GRISWOLD HOWES

INSECT BEHAVIOR

BACKYARD EXPLORATION

HAND BOOK FOR THE CURIOUS

THE GIANT CACTUS FOREST AND ITS WORLD

THIS WORLD OF LIVING THINGS

With William Beebe and George Inness Hartley
TROPICAL WILD LIFE IN BRITISH GUIANA

TO

LOUIS AGASSIZ FUERTES

IN FOND MEMORY

OF HAPPY DAYS IN THE FIELD

"Our science is a drop,

our ignorance a sea."

WILLIAM JAMES

The Varieties of Religious Experience.

EXPLANATION

Because of the many original observations recorded in this book, the technical names of the living things referred to are important. They have been included in most cases in the form of footnotes in order that they may be available at once to those who will be interested, but without interfering with the reading matter itself. The author takes full responsibility for these scientific names, they being correctly applied, to the best of his knowledge, but should errors be detected, he will consider it a favor if these are promptly reported to him. The small numbers scattered through the text refer of course to documentation and the notes beginning on page 219.

Acknowledgments

I wish to extend my sincere thanks and appreciation to the following scientists and naturalists.

Dr. Walter H. Dodge, United States Department of Agriculture, Agricultural Research Service, Beltsville, Maryland, for information on Dominican trees, Dominican flora in general, and the statement on climbing Mount Diablotin. Dr. O. L. Cartwrite, Acting Curator, Division of Insects, Smithsonian Institution, Washington, for identification of nymphal stage of a species of *Phymata*. Dr. David D. Keck, Acting Director, New York Botanical Garden, for identification of trees of the genus *Taxodium*. Dr. R. I. Sailor and Dr. A. B. Gurney, United States Department of Agriculture, Agricultural Research Service, Beltsville, Maryland, for identification of the Dominican tree cricket, *Paragryllus martini*, Guerin, and the Dominican locust, *Nesophyllidium fulvicosta* (Caudell). This species, known only from Dominica, was described in 1914 from specimens taken by the Yale-Dominican Expedition of 1913, under the name *Lichenocrus fulvicosta*, and for which a new genus was erected by Beier in 1954. Dr. Waldo L. Schmidt, Head Curator, Department of Zoology, Smithsonian Institution, Washington, for information on literature on the Collembola. Dr. William D. Clarke, Assistant Curator of Vertebrates, American Museum of Natural History, New York, for information on the eyes of cephalopods. Dr. Henry W. Fowler, Academy of Natural Sciences, Department of Ichthyology, Philadelphia, for identification of fishes, *Gambusia holbrookii, Jardanella floridae, Fundulus chrysotus, Mollienisia latipinna*, and *Heterandia formosa*. Dr. Karl F. Koopman, Academy of Natural Sciences, Philadelphia, for checking my identifications of bats collected in Dominica, British West Indies.

That part of Chapter Ten, Part I, dealing with the Dominican frog, *Eleutherodactylus martinicensis*, in unrevised form and more briefly, appeared in the *Atlantic Monthly*, and parts of the chapter on Collembolans dealing with *Microstigmus* wasps appeared in *Animal Kingdom*, published by the New York Zoological Society.

Contents

Illustrations

Introduction

THE more my knowledge of nature accumulates, the more graphically am I reminded of what I *do not know*. It is this constant awareness which has made me humble and which continues to keep me so, this incessant prodding by the colossus we call ignorance.

The longer I live and am fortunate enough to carry on, the greater is my astonishment at so many human beings who still insist that we must, and that one day we shall, fathom all of the secrets of life and the universe. Indeed this seems to be their fervent hope and wish, and meanwhile with growing tension and anxiety they wait, believing that in the end science will resolve all of the mysteries and all of their problems; yet notwithstanding their worship at this altar these people live in fear, though often unspoken, of what their technical god may yet unleash, for its most terrifying child has already caused a deep feeling of dread and *guilt* everywhere and a sharp reminder of Pandora's box which may be our salvation.

Again, I am astonished by those legions who seem to know only despair; all is hopeless chaos, humanity is lost, life is futile, man is rotten to the core. These are the unfortunate ones who feel, on the other hand, that science has already knocked the props out from under their universe, reducing them in the process to their dreary philosophies.

But there is a third and happier army of human beings also,

a growing one, an army in revolt to be reckoned with, which sees in the limitations of knowledge and science, in the physicists' wilderness of atomic particles, in the wide disagreements at scientific symposiums, in classic doctrines found suddenly in error, the necessity for a humbler appraisal of ourselves and a franker admission of our basic ignorance even in this modern day.

Many of the negative gaps are minimized or ignored, or often hidden from the layman in passages of jargon, a shield behind which science writers and investigators now too often take shelter. So involved and cryptic do these outpourings sometimes become that scientists as well as laymen despair of understanding them. As C. P. Swanson so aptly stated in *The Quarterly Review of Biology*, there is "a nebulous and almost insidious interplay upon the printed page. . . . It is no wonder that most biologists throw up their hands in horror at what to them must be unintelligible jargon." *

This book deals with common organisms in a simple manner, viewed through the sympathetic eyes of a naturalist who has spent close to fifty years in the field of natural history. Many of these organisms are abundant in the backyards or wood lots of New England; others were studied or observed in the swamps and ponds, or the woodlands elsewhere. Remoter ones dwelt high in the forests of the West Indies mountains; still others lived upon an island in Panama, in the Andes of Colombia, or in the great rain forests of British Guiana, in South America.

Wherever I have traveled or studied the living things of this world I have felt the necessity of being interested in *all* of them. We miss a great deal by specializing too much, by dismissing the tiny entities in favor of the more obvious ones because they seem insignificant, for it is the over-all picture which one gradually draws up after years of observing the

* Volume 29, No. 1, March, 1954, p. 61.

myriad little creatures and of storing up astonishing or commonplace facts regarding them, which brings full realization of the almost unbelievable intricacy of the organic network which everywhere confronts us.

My world is a happy world in which there is indeed a great deal yet to live for. I hope to carry some of my readers into this world which so few of us recognize even when it is in front of our very noses. Let us open our eyes a little wider than usual for a new look and perhaps some new experiences. Let it not be thought, however, because these observations are to be written about creatures widely diversified and variously situated upon the organic tree, that these chapters are but random sketches thrown together simply for the sake of making a book. The subjects were selected from among *thousands* of candidates, and purposely placed and woven into this volume. They are my witnesses in defense of the statement that, no matter where we look, we will sooner or later find things which are too involved for any simple mechanistic explanation. It may be this indisputable fact— that the apparently commonplace in nature often proves to be the most difficult of explanation—which has evolved the jargon of the writers to which I have alluded.

I believe that we older naturalists, who have mellowed in the field, have a mission in helping those less fortunate people who have lost faith because they see only one end to the scientific age. Through long and reverent study I believe that naturalists acquire a special kind of vision, vision which strengthens faith from day to day, a kind of vision which may be communicated to others who will listen. I believe that at least some of those who read *all* of this book will understand the message, will feel a rising tide of reverence within them. I want the reader to share my kind of delight in the myriad life which is everywhere around us, and to which I have already alluded; to see the world just outside of his or her accustomed door—whether it be in surburban New England, the remote backwoods, or in the mountains or forests of tropical lands—as it really is, with man as only a single star in an organic galaxy, and a star too often all but blind.

I wish to add what weight I may to the spiritual awakening, a renaissance which I see in the rising curve of interest in nature all over the country; in the birth of hundreds of museums; in growing wonder before the greatly expanded universe, with our former conceptions of star ages and distances enormously magnified; in the huge recurring religious gatherings, even in Russia where the church has survived; and of course here, in rising membership at most of our own churches. I see it also in enlightening books and articles, and in the uncertainties expressed by scholars wherein responsibilities are recognized and a mistrust of scientific absolutism brings an admission of the two directions or aspects which must be faced in any part understanding of the world and the universe.

Every dedicated naturalist believes that sooner or later his work and his teachings will influence some of those with whom he comes in contact toward a more humble point of view. The exploring naturalist may not go often to church himself, but in his deep personal faith in the universe and the earth he knows that no cathedral is more worthy, or as *lasting*, none more perfect or more beautiful as a place of reverent learning on his journeys than these "Green Mansions," whether at home or in the wilderness. As the late Archbishop of Canterbury Dr. William Temple once said: "It is a great mistake to suppose that God is only, or even chiefly, concerned with religion."

I look upon the universe and nature as upon an enormous, inexplicably complex tapestry, still in the process of its weaving, exquisite in the refinements even of its single threads.

We need only look at ourselves, or at any part of our wonderful anatomies, at those of any of the lesser organisms, or at the endless living associations upon the land, or in the waters, anywhere in the world around us, or in the skies above, in any microscopic fragment or in any macroscopic mass. We may only see some of these things distantly and vaguely like the markings on Mars or the minutest entities beneath our microscopes; many others we may reach out and touch, while still others we may gather in for close and concentrated observation, but all, like a waterfall, will baffle us in the final analysis with their complexity. My chapters but scratch a surface where dwell thousands of living things, encountered by the author with the moderator of our vast ignorance as a constant and leveling companion.

One day as a boy, I watched steel-blue beetles courting upon a flower. I watched the male caress the female with his delicate in-bent and quivering antennae, saw him at length accepted, then watched the two become one. Removing them to a match box, I kept the pair in my room for a day or two, using a magnifying glass as a cover. Not long after they had separated I saw the glistening eggs emerge, and so came the revelation of the meaning of sex. It was the beginning for me of a life as an investigating naturalist, a life now, as then, crowded with discovery, with inexplicable facts, with pleasant shocks.

Today there is still contentment for naturalists to be found in exploring the worlds beneath our feet, and with man seriously making ready for the exploration of outer space and the other planets, there is the more reason to emphasize how much he has still to learn about his own. Doubtless from a military, certainly from a scientific, standpoint, we must conquer space, but those who are in such haste to get to other worlds for the mere sake of the thing are like children in a museum who rush pell-mell to the top floor in noisy haste after naught but impatient glances at the exhibits below.

Let it not be thought from this book's attitude that dedicated naturalists, because of their absorption in and concentration upon their chosen work, are merely idealists unaware of the problems and evils in the world. Doubtless most of them, or at least the older ones living today, have seen the world come through from three to five wars, have contributed their labors, or have served actively in them, in some cases giving their lives like any other soldiers. But most naturalists recognize the good which still outweighs evil, have the faculty to see beyond evil and to find inspiration in the beauties of the natural world which remain unchanged. Such ascendant vision was exemplified by my late naturalist friend George Inness Hartley, with whom I shared long happy days in the forests of South America, and who, as a soldier in World War I, wrote delightedly from the battlefield of the birds there which overlooked the violence and noise of war swirling angrily around them, to go ahead undaunted with their customary seasonal nesting activities. Like most other people, most naturalists recognize all of the evils and dangers of the times, but their faith in the future may remain unshaken because there is such a thing as having it strengthened again and again through contacts wherein one comes upon things which are deeply inspiring and so complex that they cannot be dismissed with a mere shrug of the materialistic shoulders.

With this book I hope to add a little to the vision of my readers, to induce a state of mind in which all natural things will look more radiant and more significant, even the merest microscopic threads from the macrocosm, and to point out the benefits to be derived from taking more of one's leisure hours in learning to observe and contemplate the world around us more thoroughly, a recreational course which allows one to forget for the time being the daily labors and the dreary routine tasks, and which directs one to the color and melody and the wonderful interrelations of living things, and which any one may discipline himself to enjoy in a new way. Most human beings have a visionary faculty. All that is necessary is to recognize it and to cultivate it carefully.

Throughout the book I shall continue to emphasize our ignorance, for this is good medicine. Deeply moved by what I have seen, my summed experiences point for me to something so infinitely involved, something so marvelously constructed as a whole, that we shall never grasp its secrets fully in the test tubes of the laboratory. Scientists may synthesize a protein now and then and even one of the nucleic acids which forms an essential component of a virus or a gene, and then feel that they are on the threshold, but they will still be a frighteningly long way from the synthesis of a recognizable creature which swims or crawls, which eats and evacuates and reproduces itself.

The great tapestry is here for our intense satisfaction, to watch, to ponder, to be part of, and to revere as it is still being woven before our eyes. This, I have felt for a long time, constitutes the Medicine of God for those who will simply reach out and experience it.

PAUL GRISWOLD HOWES

November, 1958

This World
of Living Things

CHAPTER I

Our Ignorance a Sea

THERE is a great rhythm in the world and the universe that we call evolution. I believe, as millions do, that upon our comparatively minute planet this force, whatever may be behind its energy and its processes, labors endlessly toward the production of better organisms—more alive organisms— and now, having succeeded in opening up for one organism vast channels of perception through the human brain, we should reward this triumph by being more skeptical of its accomplishment by chance. I believe that over the millions or billions of years that lie behind the appearance of humanoid beings upon the earth, this force has brought forth, complicated, and advanced more forms of life than it has retarded. I believe that the main purpose within these individuals is, and always has been, the goal of adulthood and duplication of self, but the final goal, and whether there be one that human beings will ever fully comprehend, will remain something about which each one of us must form his own beliefs and conclusions. It is the great force called evolution, *when unhindered* making better and better use of atomic and molecular building blocks, which may, if we cease to tamper with it and cease to jeopardize the stability of our genes with atomic fall-out, guide us permanently into the ascending channel that we have all been seeking.

3

Life, we feel quite confident, has progressed from virus and bacterium and the single cell, which are great complexities in themselves, to the multicelled organisms, or Metazoa, thence forward through the geological ages, making improvements here, discarding other experimental entities there, even allowing occasional satisfactory creations such as the oysters and horseshoe crabs and 'possums to become static for x-million years, and culminating its achievements to date in the only animal capable of connected logical thought and speech—man, with his conscience, his vast *stored-up* knowledge, and his wealth of abstract ideas. Nevertheless, he is an embarrassing creature, whose sudden mental rise (in the evolutionary time scale) is still inexplicable; indeed, he is the knottiest piece of lumber in the huge biological pile. Scientists are actually at a loss for the solution, for otherwise we are quite like all of the other higher animals. But fortunately these endowments that have isolated us mentally from all the rest of the organisms have spawned this army of human beings who know that nothing could bring us to final defeat as certainly as universal acceptance of the purely materialistic point of view and the conviction that the human race has only itself to look up to.

Despite advances in the direction of understanding life in general, there are still enormous uncertainties. Investigations were announced rather recently, for instance, which some believe may yet push our own beginnings back millions of additional years. Humanoid remains, assumed to have been unrelated to any kind of prehistoric ape, were excavated at Grosseta, 120 miles northeast of Rome. In the opinions of Dr. Johannes Hurseler of Basle and Dr. Helmut de Terra of Columbia University, these excavations and finds might affect aspects of the Darwin Theory. Are we then on the threshold of a new conception, emancipation from so close a relationship with the apes, after all? * Whether such will prove to be the case or not, of course we do not know, but it is well to keep in mind how often scientists have had to change their views, and how delicately balanced our "facts" may sometimes be. Such upheavals are graphically illustrated by those remains of once classic Piltdown Man, long beloved of paleontologists, but which suddenly turned out to be embarrassing fakes. And now even the individuality of the gene has been challenged! It seems that it does *not* *always* pass on its characteristics to succeeding generations, a revolutionary upset. Suddenly a whole new mechanism may have to be taken into account in explaining genetic variability, which itself underlies all evolutionary change.†

The human cerebral cortex, as Julian Huxley says, is "the most complex system of which we have any knowledge," [1] yet it is incapable of pin-pointing our actual place in the universe, a universe in which science now admits of large numbers of other habitable worlds. Before the spectacle of billions of suns, myriads to be seen even in *one* out of endless galaxies by simply glancing overhead at night, it is easy to agree with Dr. Harlow Shapley, who states in his recent book, *Of Stars and Men,* that there may be more than 100,000,000 planetary systems suitable for organic life. Other distinguished scientists are more conservative, but nevertheless convinced. Says Huxley again in a footnote in *What Is Science?* "There is, however, the scientific probability that life [complex self-reproducing and self-varying matter] has been produced on a number [several hundred or even thousands] of other planets in our galaxy." [2]

Many of these other habitable worlds are probably much larger than our earth, and many are doubtless much older

---

* The finding of an almost complete skeleton of this manlike creature, *Oreopithecus,* was so announced, August 3, 1958.

† Announcement of the findings of Professor R. Alexander Brink, 1959, sponsored by the National Science Foundation, Washington.

also, and it is therefore conceivable that other highly intelligent beings exist, who through possession of superior senses and instruments may know a great deal more about us than we do about them, without, however, yet having the means of reaching us. Not to admit of such possibilities would be as unintelligent in our ignorance as not comprehending the chasm that exists between human beings and all of the lower earth-bound creatures. Conceding such beings, who may have left our mental and inventive status behind ages ago, we can also imagine that their combined intelligence and creativeness may have advanced and grown, through these older-world steppingstones, perhaps without even a thought about test tubes, almost to the realm of heaven!

One of the deepest flaws in the thinking of many human beings is their all-out egoism, proffering only man, in a universe where habitable planets are doubtless as common as eggs in a shad roe, as the one entity capable of the creation of life. Strange philosophers are these, who, denying that life could have been created through any other intelligence, yet strive tediously in their earthly laboratories, convinced that their own is capable of the feat.

The world needs reassuring opinions and fortification against too great a human conceit, and fortunately these are to be found. "We scientists can profit by being more humble in the face of our immense ignorance even within our own fields of special study," says Dr. Warder Clyde Allee, eminent biologist and Prather lecturer at Harvard until 1953. "We can also tone down our excessive pride in the discoveries we have been able to make, which are small in the face of the unknown." [3]

In an amazing way others raise or have raised their voices. After completing 534 pages of the facts in a great book, the late dean of French geneticists, Lucien Cuénot, expressed his underlying doubts in another simple 36 pages under the

heading, "The Uncertainties." [4] Here, after years as a brilliant scientist and after exhaustive coverage of evolutionary
knowledge, he queries: "Can one in fact harmonize the extraordinarily complex nuclear and chromosomal structure of
the Protozoa with the view that [these] unicellular organisms were the primitive group from which the more complex
higher plants and animals of today took origin . . . and is the
neo-Darwinist view not too mechanical, too dependent upon
chance, and too arbitrary in excluding the possible significance of final causes?" Cuénot's critics went so far as to suggest that his judgment was upset by his inability to explain
all problems of evolution. I do not believe his judgment was
impaired in the least, but rather, that as a great scientist and
a great human being, as he lived and learned and delved
deeper and deeper into the complexity of things, he simply
could not ignore his doubts, and before he died he had the
supreme courage to risk negating a lifetime of dedicated
scientific work in those thirty-six significant pages.

Says Professor George Wald of Harvard: "The most complex machine man has made—say an electronic brain—is
child's play compared with the simplest living organism."
This book will not dwell upon man's inventions. It is rather a
humble pointer directly away from such things as electronic
brains, guided missiles, man-made satellites, chemical synthesis, and the conquering of diseases, for these are the all-
important sort of human achievements, most of which we
feel confident will remain beneficial and which we are able
to understand and explain. It points toward those myriad
more or less common things and their processes that are
found in nature, big, little, and microscopic, and about which
we actually know so little fundamentally, things that nevertheless are all about and around us wherever we may be, and
which help to make life on earth and in our part of the universe what it is. It is mostly these little things, often of no

practical value in our ordinary everyday lives, which come
readily to hand, and which make up the bulk of this text,
that illustrate our basic ignorance so clearly.

From my own level in the world just outside my door, my
human senses impress me in definite ways which I assume to
be the truth. I see, for instance, what we call the bark of a
white oak tree and the clear, plant-filled water of a pool not
far beyond, a spring-fed pool that my wife and I greatly enjoy together, and which is the abode of countless small creatures. With my very good unaided eyes this is about all I *can*
see from where I am standing—the macro aspects of ordinary
possessions of interested property owners. At first glance my
observations of the tree and the lily pool would seem to be
limited to just that, yet I know positively, for the reason that
I own and know how to manipulate a certain marvelous instrument, combining superb lenses, man-made from such
ordinary things as sand and lime and soda, that upon and
under the bark of that white oak, and in *single drops* taken
from that small pool, there is vast activity, vast movement,
food rings, prey and predator, transformations, birth, growth,
death, decay and rebirth, millions of complex anatomies,
manifold interrelationships, and other tremendously intricate goings-on among tiny entities that constitute entire in-
terdependent animal and vegetable worlds.

How these worlds within our somewhat larger one came
into being, how they function, what their constituents are in
the last analysis, we have not the remotest dependable idea.
All we know is that they do exist, that they may be duplicated in millions of places, and that they are as remote from
us actually without the aid of a microscope as we are from
the possible life on the remoter planets. All of these minute
plants and animals live there without the slightest awareness
or need of man or his works, or a single one of his comforts,

facts, theories, or inventions. We may look into these minor worlds at will, as we soon shall in other parts of this book, but we will never know what makes them tick. (Figure 1.)

What can we say we *know* about the fundamental nature of organisms? Not very much to be sure. Let us delve very briefly into the subject.

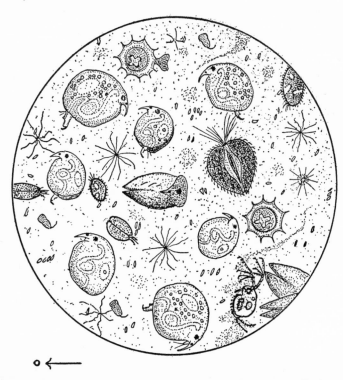

Figure 1. Culture made from swamp debris dried three years. Cladoceran is *Chydorus sphaericus,* side views and, in center of drawing, front view. Heart-shaped object is a dark-green, hairy ostracod. Crown-shaped animals are probably a species of *Arcella* (amoeboid). Hairlike stars are bright-green threads of algae beginning to grow into mats of hair. Little spiked sphere at right is *Actinophrys sol* (amoeboid). Circle at arrow shows area magnified.

We do not know the fundamental laws which dominate and control the simplest living organism. We are even ignorant of how protoplasm is organized.

We do not know when or how the first living cell was created.

We do not know what the first cell looked like, and therefore we do not know what the first multi-celled organism looked like.

We do not know how many of those all-important enzymes any one kind of cell requires and uses.

We do not know how animals synthesize proteins, including the most complex protein substances known—these very enzymes—and therefore we do not understand growth,[5] nor do we know why no two plants or animals possess the same proteins.[6]

We do not know how or when cells evolved nucleic acids, or how they produce the all-important sugar, glucose in leaves, in the presence of sunlight, water, and carbon dioxide, in the process called photosynthesis, which makes all animal life possible.

We do not know how cells differentiate unerringly in the process of forming thousands of body parts and internal organs.

We do not know why most plant cells are small or microscopic, while others such as *Valonia,* a marine alga, have cells as large as large hothouse grapes.

We do not know whether many of the microscopic forms of life—slime molds, viruses, and many others—are plants or animals.

We do not know if viruses reproduce themselves, or if they are reproduced by other living cells.[7]

We do not know how white or colored heatless light is emitted by insects, fishes, fungi, bacteria, and other forms of life, both animal and vegetable.

We do not know how the genes of any living organism record and transmit the whole instinctive experience of that organism.

We have no answer to the mystery of virgin birth or parthenogenesis, which occurs in many common organisms—*Antennaria* of the thistle family, in fungi, and various lowly animals such as the rotifers. (Chapter 4.) Here the new generations develop without the benefit of fertilization.

We do not know what causes the alteration in the number or the visible structure of the chromosomes, nor can anyone explain the movements of the chromosomes within the plant or animal cell without which cells could not divide.[8] (Chapter 2.)

We do not know how the processes evolved which made the *internal* nourishment of animal embryos possible, a great advance over the external hatching of the egg.

We do not know all of the constituents of blood plasma. No one has completely analyzed it.

We do not know why red blood cells in birds, reptiles, amphibians, and fishes are nucleated, while those in mammals, including man, are not.[9]

We do not know when the nucleus appeared in the primitive algal (plant) cell, the forerunner of animal cells.

We do not know why birds and mammals, unlike all other animal forms, were endowed with constant blood temperatures.

We do not know the exact descendance route of any living animal.

We do not know why no new phyla have evolved since early in the Paleozoic Era some 240 million years ago, an extremely mysterious fact to ponder.[10]

We do not know what controls personalities, emotions, or moods in organisms because we do not know what the regulatory activities are which go on within the brain cells governing behavior.[11]

Thus we might continue almost indefinitely, pointing out things which we do not know about the organic world. In the realm of the inorganic and the universe in general, we perhaps know even less in some respects.

We do not know how the universe was born.

We do not know what energy is, only what it does.

We do not know how galaxies evolved, nor whether the universe originated in some finite time or if it has existed forever, or whether it is expanding,[12] pulsating, or loosing galaxies at the "outer rim of space," and rejuvenating itself constantly in the center with material of new galaxies.[13]

We do not know whether the velocities of our own or any other galaxy have varied in the past or have always remained the same, nor why galaxies develop arms in some cases which take a spiral or pin-wheel form.[14]

We do not know how electric currents are generated in the stars and in space,[15] nor why the earth is a gigantic magnet.

We do not know from what depths the molten stuff of the earth arises to be spewed forth from those safety valves we call volcanoes.

We do not know what caused the glacial periods.

We do not even know what happens to a beam of light as it disappears when we direct it into the sky at night.[16]

We do not know the composition of comets. Some say they are "flying gravel banks," others that they are made up of ice particles.

We do not know what exact forces bring about these "epitomes of molecular order" called crystals, from such commonplace solutions as that of table salt and water, and dozens of other solutions of chemical salts. We wonder, too, how water hides the invisible plantlike patterns as revealed in frost, and how the latent endless six-sided designs which we call snowflakes lie hidden now, as I write this, within the flasks of water upon my laboratory shelves.

We do not know the true composition of the atom, or how long it took the chemical elements composed of atoms to form.

Physicists informed us with happy confidence not so long ago that the atom was naught but a trilogy of electron-proton-neutron, something which might be easily understood and which might explain all things in the universe, but the "knowledge" of today is often kicked rudely and bodily into the ash heap of tomorrow, and now (1958) physicists have discovered, theorized, and enumerated thirty-two "fundamental" particles, with undoubtedly more to come as time marches on. We have today a particle wilderness out of which the physicists dearly hope for someone to lead them.

Professor Hideki Yukawa of Japan and Professor Werner Heisenberg of Germany stated their dissatisfaction in 1955 with the theories which are the keystone of modern atomic thought. Science, they believe, must again seek a new explanation for the fine points of the atom's structure. They criticized Einstein's theory of relativity and the quantum theory, which after all are the mainstays of today's atomic development, as no longer sufficient. Existing theories "at best serve to give a semi-phenomenological explanation for the qualities of elementary particles, but fail to explain their existence convincingly," was the statement of Professor Heisenberg.

Despite their doubts as just mentioned, these physicists assured us that modern science *was* certain that there were no particles smaller than the neutron, the proton, the antiproton, and two other "strange particles," all of which leaves us in a skeptical frame of mind.

Theory assumes that the light substances which we call

the chemical elements combined in successive steps to form heavier ones. Helium, for instance, consists of four nuclear particles and its *atomic mass* is 4. As George Gamou put it in *The New Astronomy:* "The next nucleus should have the atomic mass 5; but the fact is that no nucleus of mass five exists; at least none of any appreciable length of life is known. For some reason five nucleons simply do not hold together." After helium 4 the next nucleus known is of mass 6. We do not know why there is no mass 5. No reaction bridging the gap has been found.

In writing thus of the things we do not know about the two worlds—the organic and the inorganic—it would be only too easy to continue without end. The truth is that this chapter had already filled thirty-odd pages and had thus run into monotony, before it was cut and finally revised for publication, but it is also the truth that in those many pages we had only begun to scratch the surface. In concluding, let us remember also that we actually know nothing of the true composition of light or the innermost secrets of vision, the very things which in concert make all of our objective observations possible.

It is of course possible that some of these things which we do not know now may be known, or believed to be known, by the time these lines are in print, and it is also possible that things which we thought we knew will have since been proven wrong. In any case the truth will remain that "our science is a drop, our ignorance a sea."

CHAPTER 2

Man and His Sperm

LOOKING squarely at nature as a whole, no one can doubt that we human beings occupy the most unique niche in the living world. As the most advanced mammalian species we embody to date by far the most intricate threads of the great tapestry, and dizzily we find ourselves swaying in the topmost branch of the organic tree. We have been endowed with a huge brain. We have been offered all the beauty of the world in which to dwell and evolve, and we are free to choose the direction in which we wish to travel, but perhaps because of the very lavishness of these gifts and offerings we have inevitably grown conceited. We forget all too frequently that our earthly *beginnings* are still of the very simplest, and that our bodily affinities here remain unmistakably with all the rest of the animals.

Let us therefore take a short refresher look at certain facts about ourselves as we are launched upon the living scene. I refer to that time which as far as mankind is concerned is perhaps the most important one of all, that fraction of time when cell union takes place, that instant after much confusion when by an orderly process the successful male sperm cell merges with the ovum or egg cell within the body of the female human being.

Here, however, we are considering an event upon which

we have no monopoly, for sexual reproduction is one of the commonest and most successful things in nature. Lower in the scale of both plant and animal life there are, of course, quite different and varied reproductive processes. There are, for instance, those microscopic protozoans called *Paramecia* (Chapter 4) and many others which simply divide their entire "bodies" in two. There are the lowly planarias or flatworms already mentioned, which divide crosswise, thus becoming two individuals, while certain starfish separate their arms which then grow into new individuals. There is parthenogenesis also, in which offspring develop from specialized reproductive cells without the need of a male, and in those animals where only the female is known they continue to reproduce their kind in an endless and baffling way. Still other methods of reproduction are by means of spores *and* sperm, as in the wood rush and horsetails (Chapter 3), or by that most convenient process of all whereby the new individual springs from detached parts of the parent as seen in the sprouting leaf or cutting, but the vast majority of the higher life forms normally depend as we do, upon the separate sex cells which merge to form a parent cell. This method is sure and efficient. It assures a merging of the inheritance factors of both parents, which in turn supply the endless minute variations in the offspring which follow.

Let us look at our own sperm cells through the high-power microscope. In the tiniest measurements of human semen there are uncountable, unbelievable hoards of them. They look like the minutest imaginable polliwogs with enormously lengthened hairlike tails. Lashing continually and energetically, these whiplike appendages propel the head containing the nucleus, and the middle piece just behind it, of each spermatozoon forward, as in dense and seething crowds they struggle toward the goal—the female egg or ovum. Here we have myriad violent and ardent microscopic suitors, which having first negotiated most of the dangers and pitfalls in the pitch-black passages of two human beings, now writhe onward in a seemingly uncontrolled maelstrom, unconscious of course, and unaware that out of all their millions only one of them will become the lucky mate of an ovum. Guided at length successfully to the egg, this single spermatozoon drops its tail and penetrates the membrane of this female cell.

Now, in one of the most wonderful events in nature, the nuclei of both of them merge, and in this imperative directive the tiny things have thrust upon them by some inexplicable force a process and experience which in its beauty and strangeness is analogous to that of the mating of the man and woman. Wrapped up in those two combining cells are the color of the future human being's eyes and hair, all of its other characteristics, all of its ability for learning, perhaps the genius of a master painter, musician, or literary giant. Once combined, the nuclei form a *parent cell* which is called the zygote. Parent cells are thus the microscopic insurance agents upon whose policies the success and continuation of the entire human family rests. From the zygote the embryo, and the new human being, arises.

Every normal male begets these spermatozoons in billions, and it is a thought worth considering that at the outset mortality is probably as high or higher among them as it is among shad or smelt sperm, for even these lower vertebrates must shed their millions over their eggs to insure the continuation of their kind.

For the perilous journeys ahead our sperm cells are made viable by subtle combinations of chemicals within the seminal fluid. In their rude jostling and shoving they require such protection, and in their determined oneness of purpose they remind us of their colossal by-products, human crowds trying as one to gain entrance into the single doorway of the greatest show on earth (Figure 2). A miracle lies in the fact that such minutiae accomplish such wonderful things. So small are these triggers of mankind that all of the sperm cells which have brought about the present population of the world could be crowded into the space of a drop or two of water.[1]

In considering the whole story of reproduction or simply touching upon the subject as I am doing here, that which

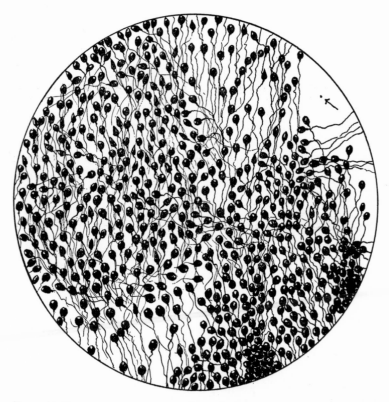

Figure 2. Human spermatozoa seeking the ovum. They are so difficult to see that they have been drawn in black. The approximate area magnified is shown as a dot at the arrow.

has not been emphasized often enough or strongly enough is the collective all-importance of spermatozoa throughout the living world. It would seem that the spermatozoon has been shunted too frequently into the side lines in favor of much larger, more obvious, and perhaps less embarrassing ancestors. Ever since Darwin's day scientists have been stressing our descent and that of other animals from simpler forms, which is all very well and proper, but the emphasis has not been strong enough upon ancestral forms which are primitive *enough*. We have been advised through the years to recognize our own apelike characteristics and relationships, and to visualize the descent of birds through reptiles, amphibians through fishes, and so on, but what has not been made clear enough to the casual reader is that all of the higher animals, most of the lower ones, and even some plants have their beginnings in these similar sperm cells, and in ova produced by the opposite sex, most of which are invisible to the naked eye.

The sperm of mouse or man, bluebird or boa constrictor, frog or flatfish, worm or wagtail, June bug or jellyfish is fundamentally the same sort of single-celled entity. We animals are terribly similar in our primitive struggling beginnings. Unless known from what creature it came, I will wager that except perhaps in cases such as the tiny bean-shaped aquatic animals called ostracods (see Chapter 6), which inexplicably possess the largest sperm cells in the animal kingdom, and a few organisms with tailless sperm, there is not one microscopist in ten thousand who could identify the multitudinous species of spermatozoa which might be placed under his lenses.

In penetrating the ovum the single spermatozoon miraculously sets in motion those tremendous processes which result in the synthesis of a new human being, with its unique, conscious, thinking brain. Remember that the sperm of honeybee or horned toad, mouse or motmot, bullbull or bullfrog, manatee or man, does *repeatedly*, yet may trigger *only* the processes which duplicate its own particular kind. This merging and triggering is the goal of the sperm cell and "goal-seeking and directiveness in organisms," says Edmund Sinnott, "should be recognized as a basic fact and as life's most characteristic quality. About it center the great problems of biology and philosophy." [2]

Remember also that in the entire world today there is but a *single species* of man. We find no specific discontinuity. Man may mate with woman of any nationality anywhere, and offspring are possible, but among the other groups of animals there exist tens of thousands of species which cannot interbreed. Something, it is obvious, has great faith in human beings, otherwise there would surely be contemporary species of the genus *Homo* now at large in the world as additional trial balloons in the race toward a better civilization.

From the instant that the spermatozoa are released, we adults have nothing more to say about the events which normally follow. The human male having deposited some two hundred million of these minute entities in the genital duct of the female [3] (about as many as there are stars in a very small galaxy), the adult mates must thereafter trust the synthesis of the new human being entirely to the know-how of the multiplying cells which their union sets in motion in the zygote.

Let us now see the events which follow the formation of this parent cell.

Every animal and vegetable cell (red blood cells of mammals for some reason excepted) contains a nucleus enclosed by a delicate membrane. Within this object there are definite numbers of granular bodies, definite according to the species involved. These rodlike bodies are called the chromosomes, and although they vary in number enormously, there are always the same number in every normal cell of every species. Within or part of the chromosomes, as already mentioned, there are also those somethings called the genes, which no one has ever seen, but which seem to be the all-important factors of heredity. Around the nucleus, and enclosed by another membrane, is the remaining living material of the cell called the cytoplasm. Each chromosome differs in shape and size from all of the others in a set. In our own case there are forty-eight in every cell.

It will be obvious to the reader that in sexual reproduction, unless something extraordinary happened to correct it, in the merging of the sperm cell and ovum to form the zygote, the newly formed parent cell would contain a double number of chromosomes. In our case there would then be forty-eight from the sperm cell and as many more from the ovum, or ninety-six in all, a condition if it existed which would upset the whole apple cart of normal development. This of course does not happen, for here by means of one of nature's most involved and inexplicable processes the number of chromosomes in each sperm cell and egg cell becomes reduced in number by one half, and thus is the normal and correct number of forty-eight re-established in the zygote or parent cell.

What do we see next when the parent cell and all of the other body cells which follow divide to create the embryo and the new organism? Thanks to our wonderful microscopes we may at least study these miracles even though we cannot explain them. First we find each chromosome swelling and finally splitting along its linear dimension, transforming, one might say, into identical twins. From somewhere there now appear what seem to be groups of threads composed of the most delicate and unknown material, which nevertheless are able to quickly draw the two sets of split chromosomes to opposite sides of the cell, an accomplishment made possible by the breaking down of the nuclear membrane. Next, the two groups of chromosomes become drawn inward and bunched together, their lead threads now vanishing as new membranes are formed around each flowerlike group. All at once the un-initiated excitedly realizes that there are now two nuclei, each charged with a complete set of chromosomes, numerically correct for the species, as the cell, also splitting its cytoplasm, divides equally into two.

Such then, in greatly simplified outline, are the cryptic phases through which each and every living cell must pass in dividing into daughter cells. Every multi-celled plant and animal that ever lived—protozoan or dinosaur, alga or redwood tree—was so erected of splitting cells, and so are all of the living things today. By learning of this exquisite fundamental process, we understand clearly and at once why every cell in our own bodies, and those in all other living things which propagate by sex cells, carry the parental inheritance in equal proportions.

Because the chromosomes exist in pairs within the cell, it was thought that there were two kinds of genes in each one also, but later researches seem to show that there is no one-to-one correspondence between the chromosomes and the genes. How these objects accomplish their endless missions in controlling all of the factors of inheritance is one of the great unsolved mysteries. "For that matter," says Dr. George Gaylord Simpson, "it is not yet known precisely what a gene is, except that it must be a unit in the chemical make-up of a chromosome and that a mutation must be a change in the structure or composition of that unit." [4] Regardless of whether they have actually been seen or not, genes are generally and widely accepted by practically all biologists today as the inheritance factors.

It is of the utmost importance in the development of normal organisms that each cell receive the exact proper number of chromosomes for the species. Experimenting and tampering with them, that is to say, tampering with nature to such an extent that the cells are unnaturally offended and forced to receive an improper number of these units, brings about abnormalities of all sorts, conditions which make for sickly freaks and even death. Herein lies the warning once more that we do not know what may come from continued atomic fall-out and radiation. If soil and animal life are gradually absorbing substances from fall-out which can affect the genes, there is no telling what the final results may be. Worst of all we do not know how radiation causes the breakdown of the body and its blood cells.[5]

I have no intention here of going any deeper into the actual machinery of cell division (mitosis and meiosis), nor into the subject of heredity. Attention is to be directed only to the splitting of the zygote and the astonishing repetitive process which follows.

As we have just seen, the parent cell divides into two. These in turn divide into four, the four into eight, these eight into sixteen, the sixteen into thirty-two, the thirty-two into sixty-four, the sixty-four into one hundred and twenty-eight, the one hundred and twenty-eight into two hundred and fifty-six, and so on and on, until countless millions are the result, each cell carrying its exact share of chromosomes and the hidden genes of the parents.

We cannot go into the tremendous details of embryological development, but the few facts which follow will doubtless astonish those who have not broached the subject, and they will serve for the purpose of this chapter.

As cleavage of the cells continues, a cluster of cells results which soon divides into two parts, a sphere of cells which is hollow, and a solid ball of cells attached to one side of the sphere within. From this inner ball arise the layers known as the ectoderm and entoderm, and in all animals except sponges

and coelenterates * a third cell layer called the mesoderm de-
velops between these other two. Remember that we are skipping hundreds of details in the process of development, but
the astonishing fact to be digested is that these three layers
of cells now proceed to evolve in some way, all by themselves,
all of the necessary parts of a new living organism. From the
ectoderm arise the hair and the nails and the skin, the sweat
glands, the lens of the eye, the mouth lining, the nostrils and
the anus, the enamel of the teeth, and the entire nervous
system: the brain, spinal cord, ganglia, and nerves, and the
receptor cells of the sense organs.

From the entoderm cells come the gut lining and the lin-
ings of the trachea, bronchi, and lungs, also the liver and
pancreas, the lining of the gall bladder; the thyroid, para-
thyroid, and thymus glands, and the lining of the urethra and
urinary bladder, while the mesoderm or middle cell layer
creates the dermis of the skin, the muscles, the bones, cartilage and connective tissue, the dentin, the mesenteries, kid-
neys, testes and ovaries, the blood and all of the blood
vessels as well.⁶ When we stop to remember that wonderful
as the accomplishments of the cells may seem in our own
case, we are only one among hundreds of thousands of living
things which cells can build. Without a doubt their self-
duplicating ability and their ability to differentiate into all
parts of all bodies was not only one of the most successful
inventions of nature, but remains one of her greatest mysteries
as well.

After millions of years of evolution, all plants from the
lowly *Pleurococcus* to the giant *Sequoia,* all animals from
amoeba to man are physically no more than cells, whether
single ones like some algae and infusorians, or vast aggregates such as the redwood trees and ourselves. We think very
little about the units of which we are made, these tiny cells

* Hydras, jellyfishes, ctenophores, or comb jellies, etc.

and their work, but these billions which summed make a human being or a bluebird or a mouse must co-operate in every slightest demand of the bodies which they have created, must obey implicitly and instantly like the individuals of a superbly disciplined army, each and every one of the commands which pour endlessly from the general headquarters of the brain.

From all of these mysterious procedures we may single out two, which, to the author at least, seem the most baffling. First, a man and a woman, a stallion and a mare, a cock and a hen, a drone and a queen—the male and female in fact of any living species—have nothing to say about the work of these units. Cells do the whole colossal job superbly and unerringly. As a great and highly skilled labor force they perform their miracles in total darkness and in total ignorance of the strange and often intelligently conscious edifices which they are erecting. Secondly, and to repeat it for emphasis, we have the final miracle of inexplicable units capable of duplicating these orderly processes over and over again once they are directed to their labors by the simple act of coition. This last great truth would seem to annihilate any argument that existence is but the result of chance, for these endless repeat performances of the cells, accomplishing what they do as everyday tasks, has baffled all scientists down to this day. There is no denying that for all living stuff there is the *goal* of adulthood.

Before concluding this chapter let us recall once more the humbling fact that in our beginnings we have much in common with the jellyfish and the worm, the fish and the amphibian, the reptile and the bird, and all of the other existing species of animals. Like most of these, the human being begins as an object far less in bulk than hundreds of microscopic protozoan one-celled creatures which even in crowds find ample room in single drops of water. Indeed there could be whole populations of some of them in single drops whose every individual would greatly dwarf the struggling spermatozoons of man. A single *Rotifer* or even *Paramecium* from cultures such as I have described in Chapter 4 could trample hundreds of these polliwoglike human sex cells all at once. (Figure 3.) This is exactly how we proud human

Figure 3. Rough outline sketch of a rotifer (*Euchlanis*) magnified two hundred times. At right, human sperm cells under still greater magnification.

beings begin—as single-celled atoms of living stuff, knowing nothing of the huge bodies and brains to be initiated, or the world in which those so created will dwell—as subspecks which could be engulfed most easily, but without supplying much nourishment, by the invisible protozoans of the rain puddle. Could we, even as conscious spermatozoa, live in such an environment, we would not need to be frightened. Being so very insignificant as food potential we would doubtless be overlooked.

In another light, however, the picture is much brighter, especially when we return to the subject of our brain, for while we commence very simply like other animals, our particular kind of cells were somehow endowed with the sacred secret of accumulating into fabulous aggregations and forming convolutions within our expanding skulls. How unique is our acquisition will be better realized when we think first of the newborn child. Wonderful as a baby may be, its mind is at first as empty of understanding as that of a calf, yet unlike any other living thing, within a few years this brain may master most of the handed-down learning of the human race.

In a few thousand years of man's existence as a conscious and planning animal he has been involved in too many wars, and he has made many other serious mistakes, but on the whole he has benefited from the size of his greatest gift, his brain. If he continues to search out and recognize his responsibilities, and succeeds in transmitting this sense to the less scrupulous leaders of the still misguided portion of the human family, all doubt as to his supreme climb, both mentally and spiritually, will be finally swept away. For such a destiny I believe man is headed through a system of "impulse and impetus, order and a guiding law," * set up by a greater power than we know, and through which evolution has carried on its endless experiments and progress.

Having now pointed out many truths in this chapter, some of which may at first thought seem more flattening than flattering, I hope the reader will accept them realistically, appreciate his primitive beginnings, and at the same time his miraculous physiological and mental developments thereafter the more thoroughly. If so, a further journey into this book will be more profitable and enjoyable, for it is to be taken in

* Harrison, George Russell. *What Man May Be,* p. 239.

the humblest spirit, with appreciation for all living things, without the expectation that any mysteries will be solved, but simply to observe with a profound sense of satisfaction, wonder, and reverence, additional complexities which I shall continue to call threads from the tapestry.

Ballet of the Spores

SKIPPING abruptly from human reproduction to methods of reproduction employed by an ancient but still living form of plant may seem to some a curious choice for the main subject of Chapter 3, but I have written this study with care, and so placed it purposely in order that the reader may see at the outset how involved is sex in both kingdoms, regardless of whether we look into the lives of the highest or the more primitive organisms. There are relationships between animals and plants in this chapter also, which the most casual reader will discover, and which will supply food for additional original thought. Let us move therefore to a spot a few miles northwest of my home in South Norwalk, Connecticut, where three very interesting habitats are to be found almost side by side, one of which is the abode of the star of this essay, the primitive woodrush or horsetail.

The place to be visited is my favorite oasis. I call it such for the reason that among the handful of remaining natural sanctuaries in my immediate region, this particular bit of terrain is most productive for biological study. For over thirty years I have been visiting this land which has somehow managed to retain its present character. It has remained almost undisturbed by man, I imagine, since the one-time farmers gave it up as hopeless. Now long devoid of human habitations, wildlife has taken over—skunks and woodchucks, foxes and raccoons, rabbits and weasels, meadow and jumping mice—and, somewhat later, many white-tailed deer.

The land boasts a varied avian population also; prairie warblers and field sparrows, towhees and pheasants in an open part of the habitat, Wilson's thrushs in the part where woodrushes grow. An interesting flora has gradually developed, an association quite at variance with that which originally existed before the forest was cleared and the smaller rocks and boulders were stone-boated behind oxen to be deposited in rough stone walls, whose now unattended and tumbled remains still trace the borders of long-abandoned fields and barnyards.

Upon its heights this is a land of rocky outcroppings. In its intervening swamps grow pitcher plants and sphagnum moss. Its old fields are cedar dotted, their lower branches evenly winter browsed by deer. Clumps of sweet fern hide the bases of boulders which were too heavy to move, and slender birch clumps gleam brightly at every season. One wonders why anyone ever tried to conquer this rock-strewn land in the first place. Today there remain vague cellar holes grown over with brush and brambles. At their corners where once stood farm houses, a few stones and lilac bushes, still in place, peer through the tangles. Even lonely graves are here of people like Silas and Mary Brown, who, already at goodly ages, were laid to rest in the eighteen-twenties close to where they had lived and loved and tilled the inhospitable land.

Not far from their lichen-mottled headstones, their abandoned barn remained upright for decades, only to collapse suddenly one spring during my earlier years. Adhering to the inside of one partly shattered wall I found faded bill sheets, not of some long disbanded circus, but the lithographed announcement of a touring military band. Looking back now,

I realize how long that old barn stood up, for stamped upon the sheets were the almost photographic liknesses of bearded veterans of the Civil War, each man clutching a horn of curious form. This whole family of horns forming the band, even the ancient cornets, were upright models in the form of the tuba. For some reason these obsolete instruments reminded me, absurdly enough, of big yellow molluscs—papa and mama with all of their smaller brassy offspring.

When the glaciers moved from the north and passed southwest across these very lands thousands of years ago, they scoured and scraped the rocky ridges, leaving in their ponderous wake telltale grooves and scratches, crushed and broken stone, and such familiar boulders of all sizes as now dot or crowd New England woods and fields. Today on these ridges high above the intervening swamps we find soil factories in full production. Here are long beds of crumbling sandstone interspersed with squarish fragments of pure white quartz, the latter lying in almost orderly rows, where as fractured harder seams they lie exposed after thousands of years, eroded out of the softer rock. At present these beds of disintegration are of great interest, not only from a geological standpoint, but for the reason that if we look very carefully, we may observe still other and much smaller soil factories operating *within* these primary ones.

Quartz is one of the hardest minerals. Examine some of these solid fragments under the microscope and in their tiniest cracks and scratches one may find minute black specks of lichen forming pinpoint colonies already in possession and somehow finding footholds. These tiny plants enter crevices which even the instrument has difficulty in picking out. They are living there nevertheless upon this hard stone, and in their patient, tedious manner they are very slowly opening, possibly by means of tiny potions of acid, still tinier doors to the elements, to rain and wind and abrasion, to heat and frost, all workers in rock destruction, armies which collectively have leveled the loftiest mountains of the earth.

Observing these sandy slopes still further, we find small dark masses an inch or two in diameter, raised like tiny hills upon a plain. These are larger lichen colonies, growing, spreading, metabolizing, reproducing, and finally, by adding the elements of their dead, also aiding the tedious evolution of the soil.

Below the ridges, these initial, all but barren spots are succeeded by growths of hardy grasses, by sensitive ferns, and beds of reindeer "moss," which is another lichen.* Here also are other plants of the same group, one thickly dotted with bright-red fruit stalks, another gray-green, studded with tapering fairy goblets.† All three of these organisms are plant associations of great interest, and as we shall see, all lichens are really plant partnerships.

Soil is in the making everywhere upon these old ridges, and gradually it grows richer toward the bottom of every slope. In June such wonderful creations as the devil's bit waves its long white tapered flower stalks in hundreds above the tall grasses. In summer, standing clumps of butterfly weed and isolated blooms of wood lilies lure the silver-spangled *cybele* and *idalia* butterflies, while in the fall the rare fringed gentian is an annually rewarding sight.

Let us examine the *Cladonia* lichens of this habitat more carefully. A lichen, you may not have been aware, is a dual personality. It is not an individual plant, but an alliance between an alga and a fungus, an intimate partnership in which each member seems to be necessary to the other. This is called a symbiotic mode of life, and we are far from under-

---

* *Cladonia rangiferina.*
† *C. cristatella* and *C. cornucopioides.*

standing how such partnerships began. Why certain plants blend themselves thus, no one can say.

Like the higher green plants, an alga is capable of food manufacture by the process of photosynthesis. Each algal cell has within itself a chloroplast * which is the seat of photosynthesis and sugar formation. That familiar emerald haze upon a weathered shingle roof and that green tinge upon the trunks of trees, so noticeable after every rain, is due to the presence of millions of cells of a microscopic alga named *Protococcus*, a primitive species which finds such situations to its liking. By examining it closely we see what the single algal cell is like. When mature, *Protococcus* is rounded and solitary; when multiplying, it forms groups of two or more. It is so small that even with a microscope its structure is very difficult to make out. No one today can explain the vital properties of this vastly common alga or that of any of the other numerous and varied species. Here is an organism which is everywhere around us which reminds us graphically of our ignorance.

A fungus plant by contrast is chiefly a mass of whitish threads. Lacking that vital substance chlorophyll, it cannot prepare its own food, but it is efficient in absorbing moisture, and many fungi are resistant to alternate wetting and drying also. Although the plant proper consists of these mats of threadlike mycelia, we usually see only the fruiting bodies which expand above ground and which we know mostly as toadstools or mushrooms, or which we give other names at times. In other words, when we eat a mushroom we consume the fruit rather than the plant. In a lichen we have an association in which a fungus receives food from an alga, while the latter, it is believed, is sheltered and supplied with moisture in return. The two plants grow together in the closest intimacy. A lichen upon a tree or upon a rock which appears

* A plastid containing the green-colored substance called chlorophyll.

grayish-green may therefore be a truly green plant over which a partly transparent white one is growing. The cladonias of the fields are such dual personalities.

The third area of this wildlife oasis, the sanctuary wherein I have been accepted at times almost upon equal terms by white-tailed deer and their fawns, is a uniquely interesting spot which in size is but a fraction of the whole. It is not a swamp exactly, nor is it even actually upon the edge of one, yet it is always damp and sticky underfoot. You come upon it abruptly after passing the rather arid lichen- and flower-grown fields by way of a well-used animal trail which passes first through a thicket. Suddenly you find yourself in cool and deeply shaded surroundings. Looking down you find that the soil in the trail is here dark and tenacious, and deeply marked with the clear hoof imprints of deer.

Again we have here a different plant association, quite at variance with that of the nearby fields with their birches, cedars, and clumps of thriving sweetfern. Somewhere under this fraction of an acre lies water, seeping upward perhaps by capillary attraction, and here through the centuries an ecological island has been fashioned quite distinct from all of the surrounding land, an isolated shady habitat, an abode with dark, smooth soil, built from the disintegration of generations of particular animal and vegetable forms. From this mellow substance have sprung trees with thick canopies, shading and darkening the island's smaller life below. Here also grow tangles of thorny catbriar, through which ancient grapevines ascend like monkey-vines in a jungle, but the most arresting sight is a wide massed stand of dark-green horsetails or woodland rushes, myriads of them growing close-packed from the sticky soil.* These eighteen-inch individuals are descendants of giants which flourished in the vast oozy

* *Equisetum hiemale.*

swamps of the Carboniferous forest millions of years ago. These, and still smaller ones found abundantly in sandy places,* are all that we now seem to find regularly in Connecticut, although some thirty species are still in existence.

The plants of my "island" rise from widely branching rootstocks, the deeply ribbed slender columns collectively casting a curious added somberness over their darkened habitat. At intervals along each stem, surrounding the base of each internode, little scales hug them closely. Most of these stalks are the fertile ones topped with conelike masses of spore-bearing scales. Looking closely at the undersides of these scales, the sporangia will be seen from which thousands of spores are released, after which they look for all the world like tiny empty bottles.

In these masses of rushes there are vegetative shoots as well as these spore-bearing stems. They bear little whorls of green spiky branches and you may have seen them often in sandy places without realizing what they were. In these horsetail rushes we have one of the commonest plants living in our country, yet few people know what strange and wonderful events are initiated among them. As the wind careens them, as deer or fox trot past them, as the Wilson's thrush builds its deep cup nest and broods its deep-blue eggs among them, or as man, usually unheeding, walks among their legions, tiny yellowish puffs like the bursting of countless miniature bombshells issue from the fertile sporangia. Sometimes it looks like thin yellow smoke, but had we eyes powered like microscopes this dust would appear like a barrage of a billion colored balls. At every movement among the rushes the spore shower is multiplied, and at the same time the roughness of the stems rub against the intruder like the finest sandpaper. One remembers then that the *Equisetae* are

* *E. arvense,* the species found particularly on railroad embankments.

also known as scouring rushes. They are rich in silica, and if burned completely their ash yields a delicate abrasive powder which gave the plants this extra name. The rushes of this shady glade were no exception and they had found the means of extracting their share of this elemental substance even from this dark puttylike soil.

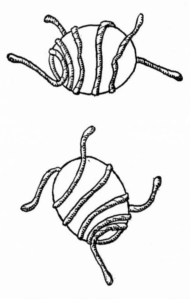

Figure 4. The spore of the woodrush becomes a hub for four appendages called the elaters. Two spores are shown, greatly enlarged.

I wondered, after examining the shoots and after burning some to observe the abrasive in their ash, if this odd family of plants could have survived down through the ages to this day, had not something beside mere chance endowed them, not only with billions of spores, but with this property of toughening themselves as well for the long long road which lay ahead of them.

Viewed through the binocular microscope, the spores

which play the most important part in the success of these rushes appear like brilliant tiny spheres, half pale yellow, half emerald green. At the proper instant when ripe, the outermost layer of every spore splits spirally, forming four white threads or stems which are club-tipped and which are called the elaters. In other words, each ripe spore becomes a hub for four appendages which are wound tightly about it like neatly fitting springs. About the twenty-fifth of April the woodland rushes cast their spores adrift from the sporangia bottles, literally in countless millions. (Figure 4.)

Beneath my lenses a pale yellowish smudge became an enormous company of free spores, fresh and moist with their birth, and each tightly clasped by its quartet of elater arms. Now as I watched, this whole company stirred, then gradually as their tiny reserves of moisture evaporated, there unfolded the most amazing ballet I had ever beheld. These minute green-and-yellow balls were like little heads and bodies all in one, while the elaters, I could imagine, were their arms and legs. The quaint little objects stretched this way and that way, as if just awakened from a long quiet sleep. Slowly the tempo increased as more and more spores joined the dance, until great numbers of the "limbs" with their swollen tips were waving in every direction. The dancers jumped and rolled, jerked and squirmed, cavorting as if for my special benefit, in every imaginable posture of the acrobatic dance and the classic ballet combined. I had never seen anything quite like this before. (Figure 5.)

Now I made an interesting observation. These spores, or their elaters, were so sensitive to moisture that even what little came from my breathing as I studied them caused all of their threadlike appendages to shrink back and coil about their respective spheres, but to reach out again almost at once and to start the dance over again as I turned my head aside and allowed cooler, drier air to sweep across them once more. This was a puzzling fact—that *moisture* caused the little springs to coil, while drying caused them to expand, the exact reverse of what one would expect, and I will make no attempt at an explanation.

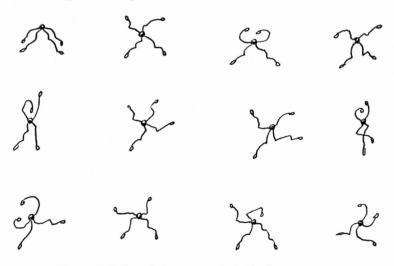

Figure 5. Ballet of the spores. Individual movements.

In a short time as I watched, all of the gaiety of the ballet ceased. Slowly but surely the dancers had frozen, each in a different final position as its arms finally dried out completely. Then all at once I had the strangest tableau beneath my lenses—living statues, numerically astonishing, microscopic in scale. (Figure 6.)

At the height of the dance which I had witnessed, many of the participants became entangled as their weird movements brought their respective elaters in contact. Indeed their minute club-shaped terminations were as mittened hands reaching out for equally willing partners. Groups formed all over the place—twos, threes, and fours—and now the smallest amount of applied moisture would cause them to huddle closer and closer together again. Here were clues to one purpose, probably the main one behind these gesturing hygroscopically controlled elaters. Their entanglements were purposeful in that they brought about the germination

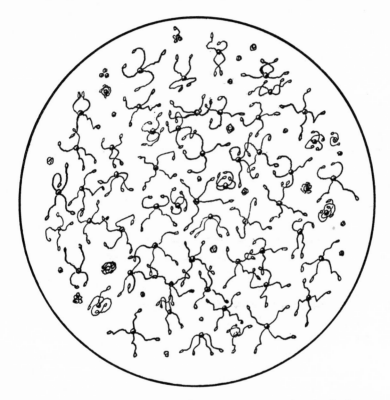

Figure 6. Numerically astonishing, microscopic in scale, the ballet of the spores is in full progress.

of two or more spores *side by side* once they had landed together and upon suitable soil. A dual, or triple, or quadruple germination thus assured the proximity of the next tiny, and all-important objects which grow out from the spores. These are called *prothalli,* and they might be mistaken by the uninitiate, even under a powerful hand glass, for minute strap-like lichens. From the flat surfaces of the prothalli grow intricate male and female reproductive organs, but usually of only one sex from any one prothallus. If male, the organs are known as *antheridia,* and if female, *archegonia.* From these separate sex organs, male spermatozoids and female ova or egg cells are released. Prothalli thus reveal that as in other pteridophytes there is a sexual generation in the complicated life history of even such a lowly plant as this woodrush.* The sperm is shown in Figure 7.

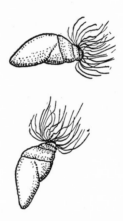

Figure 7. Sperm of *Equisetum* enormously enlarged.

As there are usually organs of one sex only arising from a prothallus, it follows, as we have noted, that the more spores which cling together and germinate together, the more certain will be the fertilization of the ova by the sperm. Although this is the life history of a common plant which we have been observing, it is still difficult to realize that from its male organs at this stage, the single-celled spermatozoids

---

* The pteridophytes include the ferns, club-mosses, rushes, and allies.

must actually *swim* over to the ova. Unlike our own single-tailed sperm cells, those of the woodrush appear under the microscope as curious spiral objects to which *several* lashing tails have been added, and like all male sex cells, those of the rushes seem to be irresistibly attracted toward the ova, in this case lying within the archegonia. As a result of the tiny unions of these two kinds of sex cells, the large spore-bearing stage, the rush or horsetail springs from the rich dark soil.

Doubtless the reader will wonder how male cells manage to swim over to the archegonia where their stationary ova-mates are located. Remember that the spores from which the prothalli arise are of microscopic dimensions and that the entire prothallus which evolves is also extremely small. A single drop of rain would easily create a water bridge of sufficient length to accommodate spermatozoids in hundreds. The slightest shower or even a heavy dew is all that is necessary to make their journeys successful.

Beautiful as the provisions for survival in the rushes may seem, they might still be defeated were it not that the spores are evolved and released in astronomical numbers. As it is, billions of them sail away upon the breezes to nowhere in particular, or to unsuitable places miles and miles away, there to die and disintegrate almost at once, yet not without serving some other minute purpose far too subtle for our groping minds to imagine, for nature conserves everything. Whatever happens, their vast numbers have made possible the rush's long history and its descent to this very time in which we also live.

The ballet of the spores, witnessed beneath the microscope, represented a truly enlightening spectacle, the mass urge of tiny entities each determined to reach out and grasp another spore and thus become entangled as intermediates in the great game of sex. Looking at a single spore and reviewing the facts—that in order to insure its kind after release, it must sail with, or land near another, must expand its elaters to grasp a contemporary, must cause antheridia and or archegonia to grow, and spermatozoids or ova to develop therein; that a spermatozoid must swim to a union with an ovum, and that all of this must be accomplished again and again in detail, thousands and thousands of times, before a great bed of tall rushes like the one in my oasis may become a fact—brings forceful realization that the urge to reproduce the species and to become adult is as strong in simple plants as it is in human beings. No one knows how many thousands or millions of generations of rushes, through their microscopic spores have successfully brought these organisms down through the ages, still tough and vigorous although reduced in size, into the world of modern man.

The alternating generations such as we have seen (one sexual, the other asexual) represent the sort of complexities to which I have referred before, which make our actual knowledge of living things appear so inadequate. Despite the self-confidence of many a learned human being, no one knows how such involved life histories evolved, but there is dogma in science as well as in religion, and many believe they understand these things just because they *wish* to believe they do.

I have written the chapter around a single organism among hundreds which could be found and studied in this one small wildlife oasis, for the purpose of emphasizing again how involved life is wherever one looks thoroughly through the open welcoming doors, and, as I have also said before, perhaps to temper the conceit of those who still think too highly of themselves and their beginnings just because they are human beings.

Closely related to the rushes living today are certain fossil plants known as the Equisetites. At the Bruce Museum we have specimens of *Calamites,* a genus of these fossils which in life looked very much like horsetail rushes of gigantic proportions. Like the little ones of our time the ancient ones also developed conelike spore-bearing organs, although they were of two different kinds. The ancient types also possessed ribbed stems, and their trunks were whorled by groups of scales just as the modern ones are.

Sometime if you have pieces of cannel coal available, break up the lumps and look carefully for minute imbedded spheres which may be fossil spores shed by tree ferns and other spore-bearers when the coal forests flourished in the Paleozoic Period millions of years ago.

It is strange, but it seems to be a human failing that people try to pin something bad upon living things. Even the innocent rush family, along with many other kinds of plants, has been condemned by certain people who carry perennial chips upon their shoulders. These spore-bearers have been accused of the heinous crime of giving horses the diarrhea, of all things. Personally it is my opinion that any sensible and normally feeding equine would pass them by without a single gustatory glance in their direction.

CHAPTER 4

Enigma of the Infusorians

No ONE knows what vast measures of time, what moods of the elements flowed over the earth, deluging it with violence, then repenting bathed it in sunlight and calm again, before a microscopic sperm cell entered the first dinosaurian ovum, and before the first monster oviduct gave forth the first great fertile egg of a *Brontosaurus*. In your imagination drift back now many millions of years and observe a brood of these giant herbivorous reptiles newly emerged from the eggs, reptiles which might in time grow to sixty or more feet in length. Observe them browsing with the adults half submerged amid the water's rank vegetation, and realize that in each mouthful which each creature swallows there might be a thousand, a hundred thousand, or a million living creatures called infusorians.

Entirely unconscious of their situation, in no particular need of knowing about it or guarding against it, they pass in a huge drifting crowd through the giant reptiles' mouths and throats. Down their enormously long neck passages they tumble, through their rumbling gaseous stomachs and intestines they swirl in a mass pell-mell voyage. In partly masticated plant matter and mud, enormous numbers pass unharmed to the vents and thence back into the very waters from whence they came. Through inexplicably transmitted instinctive knowledge, filed within the genes even of these minute creatures, large numbers shrink into resistant cysts at the first hint of these unfavorable circumstances, a process which makes consciousness superfluous, although many others perish in the rank turmoil of digestive fluids.

Back in their normal medium once more, the survivors swim forth or emerge from their encysted selves, their species and their individuality none the worse for a common experience of primitive existence. To the myriads which escape through minuteness and viability, the episode of being swallowed is of no consequence at all.

Old as the dinosaurs were in their time, as many millions of years as were required for their evolution, the infusorians doubtless antedate them by millions more. Many of them, probably little changed, have come right down to our day in numbers so vast that the stars may be their only rivals. In every swamp and lake and pond, in every roadside ditch and puddle there are incalculable numbers of them. In every field of hay and weeds, in every glade and lawn there are potential billions more. In toadstools, in lettuce and cabbages, in mosses and lichens, in aquatic plants, in the tiniest rock crevices, in the golden silk of corn fields, even in leaves and on the seeds of fruits of temperate and tropical trees there are hidden legions in one microscopic form or another. In countless places hundreds of grotesque species of these little beings are lurking, either active or desiccated, but viable as we have seen, completely unknown and unseen by the vast majority of human beings. Here we shall look into another odd and inexplicable little world, the world which Cuénot found so baffling and complex; here we shall emphasize their ubiquitous distribution and the frequent enigma even of their presence. (Figure 8.)

Just what are these things? They are members of a *primary division* of the animal kingdom, organisms contained within single cells, or a small group of cells not separable into dif-

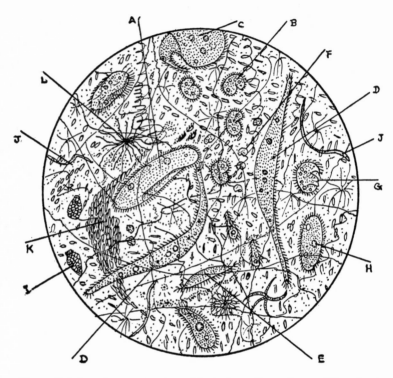

Figure 8. Infusorians and other objects from the cultures: (A) animal-like sole of slipper, *Paramecium;* (B) kidney-shaped animals, Co*lpidium;* (C) beaked creature, *Thachelius;* (D) long goose-bodied animals, *Lionotus;* (E) turtle-shaped object, *Stylonychia;* (F) small kidney-shaped animals, *Colpidium;* (G) animal with down-turned beak, *Aspidisca;* (H) tailed "wheat kernel," *Saprophilis;* (I) encysted form of *Rotifer citrinus;* (J) thin transparent worms, nematodes. Many other unidentified protozoans are shown, like those massed at (K). (L) Filimentous alga. All enormously enlarged, but not strictly in proportion to one another.

ferent tissues. Most of them being bounded by permanent membranes called pellicles, unlike the amoeba which may extend its protoplasm in any form or direction, remain in definite shapes and "bodies." Infusorians are active, predaceous little animals. These bits of living stuff are individuals, as filled with energy, as anxious to eat and as dedicated to reproduction in their way as the largest creatures upon the earth. Although but single cells in most cases, they carry on as insistently as the comparatively huge, more or less intelligent beasts, which after all are but great aggregates of single cells themselves.

Infusorians are characterized by the presence of *cilia*, encircling processes like rows of tiny hairs of various lengths, which are rapidly moved, often in perfect unison like banks of well-manned oars. With these they propel themselves forward and backward, waft food toward their mouths, and doubtless perform many additional things. Despite their apparently primitive forms, compared, let us say, to a dinosaur or a man, they are nevertheless the most highly organized creatures of their phylum.*

No living soul knows from whence or how they came to be in the first place, nor when their beginning was, but we know that they are valuable, and probably quite necessary threads of the great tapestry. Like everything else in the organic world they have their place in the nutritional ring. They are eaten by many other creatures slightly larger or higher in the scale of animal life, which in turn constitute the foods of baby fish, crustaceans, and many other creatures. They feed themselves upon the minutest of objects of their realms including bacteria, and in this association alone they constitute collectively an enormous beneficial police force which helps to keep this partly detrimental mob within some sort of reasonable bounds.

* Protozoa.

Why are they called infusorians? Because they are most easily obtained for observation from simple infusions made by rotting vegetable matter in water. One of the most widely distributed and intensively studied species is the slipper animalcule,* so named because of its outline which some-what resembles the sole of a woman's slipper. In a rich cul-ture they may be raised in vast crowds which swarm toward the surface and light in such numbers that distinct white lines, made up of countless thousands of them may be visible in rhythmic motion. A spoonful of chopped hay in a beaker of distilled water will sometimes beget them in fabulous numbers. If one or two of a single species are now removed in the tip of a hair-diameter glass pipette and placed in a fresh supply of distilled water in which a few grains of boiled rice or wheat have been standing for a few days, a pure cul-ture of this particular form may sometimes be raised in which their numbers may be increased to the millions.

Infusorians multiply by the process of fission, like our own cells, each one dividing and becoming two, the phenomenon repeating itself in the daughter cells until at times the entire culture may become overpopulated. Simple as this all sounds when written upon this page, actually in these cell divisions we see even ourselves reflected, for the nucleus of each such infusorian cell undergoes the same stages of mitosis at each division which takes place in the building of bodies of all of the higher animals including man.

Microscopic animals (except perhaps those popularly clas-sified as "germs") seldom appear to interest people because they are so little known, but creatures such as the infusorians, being nonpathological and all around us, are really wonder-fully worthwhile for study, and they seem to grow more and more complex the more we learn about them. Let us shrink ourselves down to their scale, not particularly for the pur-

* *Paramecium caudatum.* (Figure 8a.)

pose of viewing them without a microscope, but rather to compare notes with them on some points of their physiology.

Once down upon their level we see nucleated entities as strange as we might expect to find on another planet habitable by animal life. They are darting every which way in a bewildering array in their thickly populated realm. Every creature here seems to be hunting another, but in a hit-and-miss sort of manner, yet all of them, we know, are well nourished, for with our own eyes we can see the ingested foodstuffs enclosed in vacuoles and in the process of being digested, as well as the waste being gathered and made ready for ejection right through the glass-clear walls of their pellicles.

Over there are a dozen amoebae, each of an entirely different shape, and each one keeps changing its shape, yet all are of the same species. Now some of them are projecting long streamers of protoplasm from themselves and engulfing other living plant and animal cells, which we can see within them. Creatures called colpidiums are here in thousands also. If we could stop one from madly tearing about and communicate with it, we would learn that protozoans require vitamins as well as ourselves, as many as five or more kinds in some cases, but most remarkable of all we would find that there are also creatures in this swarming world which can synthesize their own vitamins. We would learn that there are infusorians here, which again like ourselves, are dependent upon oxygen, that there are others which require but little of this gas, and still others which thrive in the putrid depths of stink holes without any oxygen at all.

Most of the animals at which we are looking seem to have mere depressions or grooves for mouths, and toward these, currents of food-laden water are being wafted by beautiful banks of cilia which are arranged in all manner of rows and arcs and circlets. Some of these animals have coiled sausage-like food canals, again with visible food particles passing along them. Working herein are complicated digestive enzymes also, whose formulas are impossible of analysis, and still more deeply involved in mystery, there are animals which somehow utilize for themselves the digestive substances which they have extracted from their devoured victims. There are chemical processes involved in the infusoria which we shall never be able to explain or analyze.

As we come up into our own world for air once more, we are reminded that there are still other kinds of protozoans quite different from the Infusoria of the pond or vegetable infusion. There are even protozoans which live *inside* termites and wood roaches, whose function is to digest cellulose or other food swallowed by these insects, and which, by themselves, the much larger hosts could not take care of. With such minute creatures living within them, however, and using some of the internal substances for themselves, all live happily, well nourished, and the insects are free from indigestion.

Closely related to the Infusoria, which of course are protozoans themselves, are the flagellate Protozoa, also microscopic curious creatures which occur in enormous numbers, and which differ from the former, at least on their exteriors, chiefly in the possession of one or more whiplike lashes or "tails" in place of cilia. I have included them here, before continuing with the culture of infusorians, because of two astonishing species which cause strange *visible* phenomena in ponds and pools by their fabulous conventions.

On sunny mornings in summer or late spring, the surface of a pond or even a barnyard puddle may start changing its normal color, mysteriously alternating in shades of green and startling red. Like a colored spotlight blending very slowly into another, this red hue of the surface slowly fades by late afternoon or early evening to green once more. On the following day if the sun is shining, the red color reappears, and thus the changes may alternate for weeks at a stretch much to the mystification of the property-owner.

The cause is a flagellate protozoan, a microscopic creature which looks like an elongated baking-bean with a single long tail protruding at one end.*

Within these transparent cells the microscope reveals the presence of large numbers of bright-red granules. As the light intensity lessens, these strange objects become gradually drawn in to the center of the organism and there compacted into a mass, thus allowing equally great numbers of green particles called chloroplasts to dominate the red core. As the light grows stronger again and the day warmer as the sun comes up, the red granules again spread out widely, thus hiding the chloroplasts and so turning the *Euglena* cells and the whole surface of the pond *red*. As these organisms multiply into countless trillions, the surface of even the largest still ponds may exhibit this startling phenomena.

The other remarkable flagellate appeared in our lily pool in September. It showed up in great waves, like dark currents which then moved ever so slowly. These armies of living things formed into amazing changing patterns—bands and wavy ribbons like an aurora, long strings and ropes, almost perfect spheres, and irregular clouds—all midway between the surface and the bottom of the pool. It was as if brown pigment or pale coffee were mysteriously traveling through the water yet keeping its identity. These moving clouds contained trillions of these flagellates which is the only known species of the genus.† The tiny organisms never seemed to bump into each other, progessing in marvelous unison.

In a space one-fiftieth of an inch square (the size of the minute squares etched into my micro counting slide) 1,375 of these curious flagellates could park side by side, or

* *Euglena rubra.*
† *Synura uvella.*

3,437,500 to the square inch. If you would care to cube this figure, the result would represent the presence of something like one trillion, two hundred and sixty-six billion individuals, with still some room between them. If you would care to go on and estimate the number in a single cloud or band or ribbon, one of which in our pool measured fifteen feet in length, one foot in width, and eighteen inches in depth, go right ahead and do so. Personally I suffer intense fatigue even thinking about it.

This wonderful event commenced on September twenty-second, untold trillions of entities propelling themselves in slowly changing formations. It continued for several days, long enough for me to extract hundreds of thousands of them by means of a long glass pipette. Placed in a glass jar of water in my laboratory, these creatures swarmed in thousands upon the glass nearest to the light source and swam in miniature formations as I watched them fascinated through a microscope set up and focused through the side of their container. Greatly magnified, individuals were seen to be like spheroid masses or groups of oval balls, each object bearing numerous lashes with which it very leisurely propelled itself. A remarkable fact was that the lily pool in which these trillions came into being had been turbid throughout that particular summer, but now the water suddenly became as clear as crystal except where these living, changing formations moved through it. Did these flagellates clear it by eating up still greater hordes of still other invisible creatures? Again we do not know.

Let us leave the flagellates and return to the protozoans of my cultures once more. I believe that insufficient attention has been directed to the mystery of the presence of infusorians, in dessicated but viable form, in such a wide variety of vegetation. Their function in such things as grass and leaves is also a mystery, something which I have endeavored

to solve. In ponds and lakes and oceans we may easily visualize their status in the food ring proper, but what are such
entities as *Paramecium* and the ubiquitous *Colpidium* and
many of the other little animals described here and in other
chapters of this book doing hidden away somewhere, somehow, in one form or another, within the stems of weeds and
grasses in our meadows and by our roadsides, in the bone-
dry hay in every loft and bale, even in the mangers of our
horses and cattle? What are they doing in corn silk, or upon
acorns, or in reindeer lichens, upon boulders and the bark of
windswept northern pines? What are they up to upon the
long dried leaves and the huge rocklike nuts of great trees
of the South American rain forest?

Let us look at some of the cultures which I have made
from these various kinds of vegetation, and with a microscope examine their inmates.

From a sunny roadside at Cape Cod I took a handful of
new-mown, sun-dried hay. Tablespoonsful of this material
finely chopped were placed in sterilized glass jars of water
which had previously been boiled three times and cooled.
Within seven days, drops of this fluid contained at least nine
species of infusorians. Peering through my instrument I saw
a whole new world. First in numbers were those kidney-
shaped animalcules belonging to the genus *Colpidium* which
we will meet again and again in our travels. (Figures 8b and
9.) A much larger, grotesque, beaked creature,* its inner
anatomy exposed to my view, swam through the refuse of
the environment also, and much smaller flattish ciliates,
reminding me strongly of headless turtles and known as
Stylonychia, scurried and jerked through the debris. (Figures 8c and 8e.) In addition to these there were four other
curious unidentified organisms and many hundreds of the

* *Trachelius ovum.*

well-known slipper animalcule *Paramecium* (Figure 8a) all swarming in and out of the scum.

Now it is a very interesting fact that when I repeated this experiment with hay and weeds which were cut and dried in a field near my house in Connecticut, the same tiny creatures appeared in the cultures except for that beaked one called *Trachelius*. In cultures made from hay wherever cut, some sort of living things will spring to life, and that bad-smelling water in which cut flowers have been standing fairly swarms with Infusoria. Beside the commonest and easily observed species, the microscope, if a powerful one, will often reveal staggering numbers of what for want of their true and proper name may be referred to for convenience as gyrating dots. Sooner or later these things will be seen in most every kind of an infusion, entities so small as to be barely distinguishable singly, but present at times in truly bewildering hordes, darting this way and that in every direction as one imagines atomic particles may do. At other times they become linked together in some way in vast chains which collectively seem to twinkle like sequins on the costumes of a fabulous chorus caught in the beam of a spotlight. Again and again one encounters these things darting or shimmering in the cultures, and I wonder if anyone really knows what they are doing and why? (Figure 9.)

Through long observation I have established the fact that the smaller individuals which we call colpidiums can be found in freshly fallen rain, when the water has first passed through the foliage of woodland trees. What is more enigmatic is that I find them in droplets which remain upon lettuce and other leaves even though the rain has fallen from an unobstructed sky. My curiosity deeply aroused by these creatures of the rain drops, I decided to investigate still further.

Plucking corn silk from a ripening ear just after a heavy

rain, it was placed in a sterilized jar with a few ounces of distilled water. To my amazement, microscopic examination of the saturated material revealed that even these strands of vegetable silk were inhabited by a few small colpidiums of

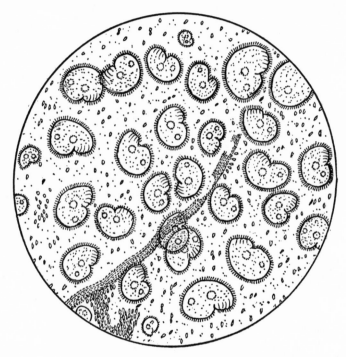

Figure 9. Colpidiums and a chain of girating dots magnified two hundred times. Seven-day culture made from hay dried for five months, then placed in distilled water.

two sizes. In another day or two those dots also appeared again in small crowds which rapidly expanded into enormous aggregations, in fact to such a density of individuals, all linked together in long vibrating chains, that in places they blocked off the culture, completely stalling the larger colpidium traffic which could not seem to breach these living fences formed of organisms hundreds of times smaller than themselves. This swarming world, this entire drama of living populations so far removed from our own way of life was observed within the thin skin of moisture composed of two

Figure 10. Colpidium baffled and stopped by dense chains of seething dots forming on the surface of culture.

drops of the culture enclosed between two thin circles of glass one-half inch in diameter. (Figure 10.)

It is always hard for me to believe that I have not been somehow mistaken when swarming cultures occur so readily at all seasons. Just before this book went to the publishers. I made another corn silk and corn leaf experiment to satisfy

myself once more. In a supermarket I bought an ear of corn
which had been lying on ice for several days. Although the
month was February, a small amount of the materials mentioned produced one of the best cultures I have ever made.
In addition to *Paramecium* and colpidiums, this one contained another oddity called *Aspidisca* which before this I
had found only in water from cabbages standing in the open.
(Figure 8g.)

To revivify some of the dry and brittle reindeer lichens
brought from my favorite oasis one day in March, they were
placed in a dish with a small amount of thoroughly boiled
water. In a week the half-inch of fluid had turned to a turbid
yellow color, and upon examining a drop with the microscope
I found it to be alive with protozoans, all propelling themselves hither and yon with their cilia in a scene of great
animation. Thousands of mere specks—again the gyrating
dots—darted about also, not having yet formed their chains,
while still other single cells, in this case, I believe, motile
plant cells or algae, greatly enlivened the spectacle. Here
was a vast milling multitude, joyous, one could almost believe, at sudden release from their dessicated prisons.

The largest and strangest inhabitant yet now appeared
suddenly from behind a bit of vegetable debris. It slid back
and forth and around and around the object as though magnetized to a rotating center, reminding me very much of a
toy I once owned which came from F. A. O. Schwarz, 23rd
Street, a turning magnetized spindle in the center of a little
round box, about which pins or wire clips or little human figures on metal bases behaved exactly like these infusorians
which as yet I have not identified. Still other curiosities were
the "goose" infusorians, creatures which might be described
as looking like well-stretched microscopic bodies of these
birds, with tiny eyeless heads. Picture these things swimming

under the surface in a corkscrew course and you will gain
some idea of this strange, strange animalcule.* And then
there were those minutiae like flattened kernels of wheat and
bearing short mouselike tails, entities so small that the water
film drawn up a single lichen stem was as deep comparatively
as the water in a lake would be to a human being.†

In addition to all of the infusorians, a much larger and
much more highly organized multicelled wheel-animalcule
or rotifer now came upon the scene, a perfectly transparent
animal possessed of definite internal organs and perhaps
even a very primitive brain.‡ These particular rotifers progressed by extending their head ends, fastening onto something and then drawing up the rest of their extended bodies
sharply, and repeating the process over and over again in
search of suitable anchorages. At each side of their heads,
retractile stalks could be seen, each bearing a cilia- or hair-
encircled disk. When all of these hairs were in motion they
gave the illusion when viewed through the microscope of
rapidly revolving wheels, and it is from these characteristic
objects that the large rotifer group of animals take their
name. Currents set up by these "wheels" waft food particles
toward the animals' mouths, which in turn lead to cavities
with muscular walls. This cavity of a rotifer is called the
mastax, wherein are located a pair of highly ingenious and
complicated jaws or trophi, very much at odds with those of
larger and more familiar animals. They may be seen rapidly
opening and closing and grinding food as in a crushing mill.
In fact the combination of the rotifer's "wheels" and its trophi
viewed through the transparent body walls gives a vivid im-
pression when in full motion that here is some curious man-
made machine of unknown application. This species called

* *Lionotus wrzesmowski.* (Figure 8d.)
† *Saprophilis agitatus.* (Figure 8h.)
‡ *Rotifer citrinus.* (Figure 11.)

citrinus is only one among dozens of different and grotesque known forms.

From long study of the protozoan fauna, especially the colpidiums, but not excluding the "goose" animalcules, the "wheat kernels," and all of the rest, it seemed to me again and again that these living things might have descended in rain drops, first carried aloft from some other part of the land in the form of dust, and later brought down again to be lodged upon leaves or weeds or hay or lichens or any other

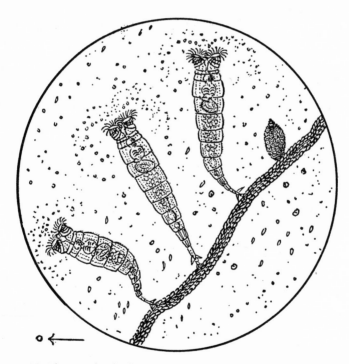

Figure 11. Three individuals of *Rotifer citrinus* with "wheels" in action feeding. An encysted rotifer at right. Culture from rock puddle and rain water. Circle at arrow shows area magnified.

kind of vegetation, and of course upon the soil itself. I believe also that such minute species as the smallest of the ubiquitous colpidiums may live between the top and bottom cell layers which constitute the outer surfaces of every leaf. Entering by way of the guard cells which are located at every stoma or leaf pore, thousands of them sometimes on a single leaf, these infusorians might find ample moisture to sustain them *inside* these guard-cell doors in the spaces between the cells. When the guard cells open, as they do in a moist or rainy atmosphere, the little creatures would be free to enter or exit, and they could easily "hole-up" within a stoma before the leaf or other vegetable surface dried and the guard cells closed again. As far as I am aware, this is an entirely new supposition in biology and as yet I have not completely verified it to my satisfaction. Here, however, I believe will be found the solution of the mystery of the presence of infusoria on many kinds of vegetation, which appear almost as soon as it becomes wet.

I have found infusorians in the strangest places imaginable. On the back of a turtle which had long been dry in the sun of Florida, in flat lichens which grow on rocks, and even in the hollow sectional joints of the *Cecropia* trees on the island of Dominica in the West Indies. Still others were begotten from the bark of a pitch pine tree at Cape Cod, from ferns and chopped-up iris leaves at home, and a stagnant acid puddle in the spruce forest of lonely Bonaventure Island in the Gulf of the St. Lawrence River (where the great gannet and other sea-bird colonies nest) yielded very large colpidiums fifty microns in length,* strange flask-shaped entities known to biologists as *Enchelys,* and another species of rotifer, a stout creature of the genus *Enchlanis.* (Shown in Figure 3.)

In one of the rock-lichen cultures a strange event took

* A micron is equal to one-thousandth of a millimeter.

place. Some weeks after it had been started, the water suddenly changed to a clear pale-orange color, and what the microscope now revealed astonished me afresh, for in every drop of the solution infusoria were *absent,* but in their place were great crowds of another sort of creature belonging to an entirely different phylum. These were microscopically wormlike, and they belonged to the great class of nematodes which occur all over the world, either free-swimming as these were, or in the soil, or as parasites living within plants and animals. There are hundreds of species of various sizes, and they are among the most numerous of the smaller organisms.

The complicated inner structure and the organs of the nematodes, including the separate sex organs, may be distinguished only with a microscope, but their details are not important here. The interesting, hard to believe fact, aside from their sudden appearance, was the fabulous multiplication of individuals. In one-half inch of the orange-colored water in the bottom of a pint preserving jar, I estimated that there were several million of them, like microscopic bits of extremely delicate thread, tapered to a point at both ends, transparent, and measuring but a small fraction of a millimeter in length. (Figure 8j.) *

In your mind multiply even a thimbleful of this population by the possible nematodes in all of the ponds and swamps, lakes and puddles, gutters and drains, soil and lichens, other plants and animals, and you may visualize their actual numbers. Even in the small culture jar we may well wonder how so vast an assemblage found nourishment, but the fact that this turbid medium became perfectly clear, like the water in our lily pool cleared under the influence of the flagellates, suggests the possibility again that many small forms of life are still to be investigated for their abilities as destroyers of

---

* A millimeter is equal to .03937 of an inch.

other life. New antibiotics may be hiding in the least expected places.

A few more observations on the rotifers should be of interest here, for they are indeed remarkable little creatures,
some even inhabiting the smallest cracks in the rocks, as
well as all ponds and swamps. In the dry powder taken from
small cracks and crevices in the rocks around my home in
Connecticut, the microscope revealed rounded pink-colored
objects, some of which had bluntly pointed ends, while others
appeared to be tiny faceted balls, shiny and translucent.
When this rock powder with these objects was immersed in
water on a microscope slide, the faceted balls proved to be
the encysted bodies of that leachlike rotifer *citrinus*. Almost
at once these objects commenced to move and expand under
the influence of moisture, and within three to five minutes
they became fully extended, their "wheels" of cilia in full
motion, their mastaxes grinding, almost as if each animalcule
knew that it must make all haste to nourish itself before its
powdery niche should dry up once more. Thus do the rotifers
"come to life" all over the world after every rain, quickly
stock up with fuel, and then encyst again as the rain water
evaporates. What do they find to eat in their puddles in the
rocks? How long have they or their ancestors peopled the
rocks? Whence came they in the first place? Again we do not
know.

What amazing vitality these little animals possess! Before
I wet the rock-crack powder, a mild puff from a human lung
might have easily launched it into the atmosphere with all
its dessicated life forms, there to travel upon the breezes and
air currents, for one, or a dozen, or a thousand miles. Indeed
I had to move and breathe very cautiously in making the
transfer to the microscope slide. Once again in this observation we have a strong clue to the distributional puzzle of

microscopic life—it can be carried by the wind to suitable new pastures.

And now in concluding this chapter I wish to record what to me was the most astonishing case of all.

Upon returning to the museum from the forests of British Guiana in 1922, I had packed away a box of large dried jungle leaves and seeds, and some of those rock-hard nuts of big forest trees which were as large as my fist. These had been picked up from the forest floor along the Cuyuni River, and had been stored for later use in a museum exhibit. In 1955, one of these leaves, half a walaba seed, and a large reddish nut were placed in distilled water in a large covered jar. In three days a whitish scum began to form on the surface of the water, and in this, with the aid of the microscope, a single *Colpidium* was discovered. This was hard to believe, but it was but the beginning, and nine days later this culture was richly inhabited by these infusorians.

For *thirty-three years* this box of leaves and nuts had lain in the unheated attic of the museum completely dried out I thought. During all of that time, through successive heat and cold of summers and winters, the encysted bodies of these things had managed to keep the spark of life aglow. Whatever the magic fuel may be, fuel which had remained deeply banked for a third of a century, it was suddenly fanned into full flame once more by the simple addition of moisture. Before such revelations I bow in reverence, not only before the miraculous viability of these cells, but before the properties of the world's most wonderful possession—water.

In leaving the infusorians let us not forget that whereas they are but single cells in most cases, they nevertheless exhibit most of the major characteristics of living things in general—swimming or creeping about, nourishing themselves by finding the proper foods, absorbing them and acquiring

their vitamins, excreting waste products through their vacuoles, and reproducing themselves with great insistence. Remember also that they are without nerves or any of the major
organs of higher animals, yet each infusorian performs the
necessary functions, which in the more advanced creatures
require the combined efforts and abilities of billions of cells
in unison. In observing the life of single cells as we have in
this chapter, we are therefore less surprised at their feats
when massed in much larger entities, yet here they have their
shortcomings also I suppose.

We have only looked into an infinitesimal part of the story
of the Infusoria, much less into that of Protozoa as a whole.
When we think of the intricacies of their chemistry and the
complicated systems which have evolved all of the foods
necessary to the thousands of kinds of these animalcules, we
realize how really ignorant we are about it all.

Infusorians are supposedly important historically because
most biologists believe that for the most part the higher animals evolved from organisms which were similar to protozoans
of our present day.[1] The reader may form his own conclusions, but actually we do not know for sure *from what* we
evolved.

The more we study these creatures, however, the more we
may make interesting speculations concerning them. They
are so numerous in vegetation, for instance, that we cannot
truthfully state that many so-called herbivorous animals are
strictly such. The naturally herbivorous creatures consume
billions of infusorians and other forms of animal life along
with their plant food. Horses and cattle and other grazers eat
trillions of them in fresh or dried grass, hay and weeds, as
well as enormous numbers of tiny but highly nitrogenous
insects. Moose and muskrats consume millions of infusorians
while browsing beneath the surface of ponds and lakes, as do
reindeer when feeding upon lichens, and ducks and other

water birds when dabbling in algae. Infusoria even fool vegetarian human beings by lurking in their salads.

Collectively their work must be of vast importance, and maybe because of their great success as a whole these creatures have not changed very much during the past millions of years of their history. Such resistant and viable organisms would scarcely need to, so probably we are not descended from ancestors anything like them.

That man, the best animal that *massed* cells have been able to erect, should die of hunger and thirst so quickly and so easily, while these microscopic single units may somehow remain waterless and foodless in quite unnatural surroundings for decades unharmed, is of course the central point of the enigma of the infusorians. These cells must have something which human cells have not, and in this one respect at least, the little animated objects in these cultures are our superiors. Do they hold the secret of eternal life? We do not know.

In contemplating all we have observed in this chapter, I am moved to repeat that penetrating sentence of Dr. William Temple, late Archbishop of Canterbury, who said: "It is a great mistake to suppose that God is only, or even chiefly, concerned with religion." [2]

World of the Collembolans

AMONG the strangest and commonest minutiae, unknown to most of us, are those extremely primitive, frail, but energetic bits of life called springtails, the apterous (wingless) Collembola whose curious world we will now explore. (Figure 12.)

Collembola live all around us in countless numbers. Once aware of them you may see them again and again, but only with a magnifying glass or a low-power microscope will you ever know them intimately. That black mass at the edge of the pond or lily pool which seems to evaporate like smoke and then gradually settle once more upon the surface of the water may be an enormous convention of them, black animated pinheads, which at your approach have unleashed their powerful underbelly springs and momentarily hurled themselves in grand abandon into the air. Those myriad shining specks which dance about like crazy when you thin the lettuce plants in spring may be brown or gray or bronze-colored collembolans, or gorgeous glistening ones sheathed

Figure 12. Top: Two mold-thread mites (invisible to the naked eye) and a still smaller one riding on a single hair (at arrow). Center: Collembolan eggs anchored by threads which may be mold, enormously enlarged. Bottom: Outlines of various collembolans, greatly enlarged.

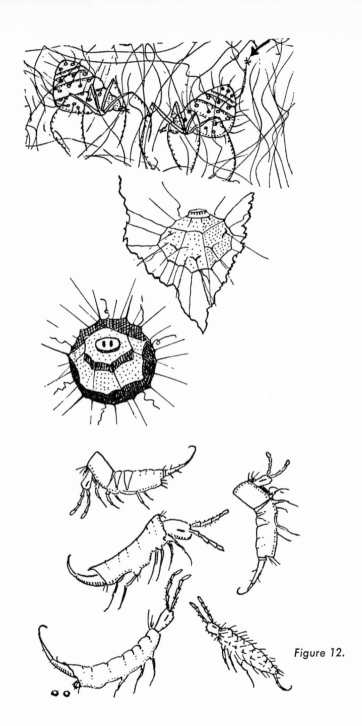

Figure 12.

in metallic violet armor. On bark and upon damp woodland floors and in rainy jungles live billions of others. Every lawn and field of grass is alive with them, slender ones or squatty gnomelike species, all with bright black eyes. Cows and horses and all other grazers swallow them in millions. Still other collembolans live upon toadstools, under stones and logs, or in moss or ferns, or upon flowerpots, or in vegetable debris, even upon cacti, and upon the snow and the glaciers of high mountains they are sometimes found in thousands.

Some of the collembolans are varicolored world travelers. The costume of a single species may be dark green or yellowish-green, yellow or lilac, blackish-blue or reddish-purple, deep purple, or even brown with pale dorsal spots to boot.*

The range of this astonishingly colored ubiquitous little creature constitutes a refresher course in geography. In its typical form it has not only been found throughout North America and Europe, but in Mesopotamia and Mexico, Northern Siberia and Nova Zembla, Spitsbergen and Bear Island, Jan Mayan, Iceland, and Greenland, the Northwest Territories and Alaska.[1] To discover that this vulnerable soft-bodied, wingless, defenseless and delicate-appearing creature boasts a world-wide distribution in identical form is amazing, and when we know that collembolans are found on beaches and *on* the oceans as well as in all of the other places mentioned, we may only conclude that the currents and winds have played their parts in this tremendously interesting distributional story. Surprising also is the fact that despite its great range of color phases this species has been allowed to retain its single species status by the hair-splitting specialists in nomenclature.

Let us look into the realm of another often gregarious

* *Isotoma viridis.*

species, which, among other places, lives in the bark furrows of the white oak tree mentioned in the opening chapter.*

So frail and tender that even a short but thorough drying of their minutely hairy skins causes them to pull in their six legs, protrude their catapults, roll over and die, collembolans are nevertheless unaffected by cold, and their bodies must be supplied with some wonderful organic antifreeze. During these investigations the thermometer often registered from thirty down to ten degrees, yet these springtails were found huddled, but unharmed among the bark furrows, handy for collection and study and now easily captured.

Lifting up strips of their bark habitat and flipping groups of them into a vial with an artist's brush, a herd of fifty of them were soon transferred to a small tin box with a clear glassine cover, which had been made ready in my study beforehand. In this box a natural environment awaited them, complete with alga-grown bits of bark taken at random from the white oak in the woods. Now stocked and ready, the whole observation box could be placed under the lenses of the binocular microscope for study at leisure.

Now as to the dimensions of these collembolans. If we could retain twenty-five of them in a neat row, head to tail, the resulting chain would measure under an inch in length. They are therefore among the smallest creatures which we can see, although not in detail, with our unaided eyes if we look sharply in their known haunts. By way of an amusing contrast, there was a comparatively Gargantuan animal, although in our eyes one of the smallest mammals in the world, which lived in a burrow at the base of the very tree on which these collembolans were found. This was a short-tailed shrew, a species measuring some three inches in length, but as ravenous a carnivore in its greatly reduced scale as an African leopard on the rampage. Shrews look like miniature moles

* *Entomobrya multifasciata.* (Figure 12.)

with sharp-pointed snouts. They remain hidden most of the time, showing themselves but rarely until after dark. Feeding upon insects, grubs and worms, and even full-grown mice three times their size, their presence is seldom realized by the majority of human beings.

The collembolans and this silky, gray-furred mammal at the base of their tree set up an amusing train of comparisons which even included me in the picture, for I calculated that if a man were the size of the collembolans in their bark world, this shrew would represent a carnivore some four hundred and fifty feet in length, dwarfing the greatest dinosaurs of the past, while I myself, standing beside their tree, would represent a monster reaching thousands of feet into the sky. Such is the world of animals!

Less than three hundred years ago, before Anton Leeuwenhoek invented and produced his early microscope, no human being could have known accurately what the collembolan world or that of any other minute creature was really like, yet today with his invention greatly refined, I may peer deeply into the springtails' most secret establishments, project myself at any time into their intimate midst and thus into habitats as strange perhaps as some might look to us on distant planets. In fact I would not be at all surprised if the primitive vegetation pictured by some scientists as existing upon Mars, and that of the bark furrows when magnified would have much in common at first glance.

What I now saw through the glassine box cover under the microscope was a bright and entirely different realm from the macro realm in which I had collected the enclosed creatures. All of the familiar things of their habitat—the tall oak tree, its simple gray- and greenish-hued bark, the very woodland itself—no longer existed. The landscape was now a series of long rugged ridges between which slumbered deep crevices and somber valleys all clothed and dotted with the strangest of shrubs. Here and there were larger, dark nubbins of unfamiliar growths, and infinitely small vermilion, iridescent, and even rainbow-tinted specks of living matter which I wondered if anyone could really name or explain.

About these hills and valleys ran hairy collembolans, as unique and unknown to most people as creatures which have long since been extinct. Some were colored green, their almost transparent gullets filled with masticated shrubbery, while others which had recently defecated were lighter in color and marked with brown. All had two rows of eight bright and shining eyes, and when one became annoyed or frightened during its periodic wanderings, it could trigger that powerful forked spring beneath its body and be flung in an instant under normal conditions, like an ejected jet pilot, far out of harm's way. Within the box, my charges were of course restricted. Out of all danger their springs remained folded, but if allowed out, the slightest shadow sent them leaping in all directions. Strange as it may seem, these tender things may be flung a hundred or more times their length by these powerful catapults, yet they employ no safety devices for landing. They require no special guards or padded suits or parachutes, for they land lightly and unharmed upon their six outstretched legs.

Along the rough and uneven highways and valleys of their bark-filled cage my charges moved at times like little vehicles on primitive roadways. Like tiny cattle others stopped to browse upon algae or wood cells, or simply rested, while still others performed head-bobbing, antennae-fencing routines which may indeed have represented their courtships. Exactly three weeks after the first collembolan colony was confined and placed under constant observation, eggs were discovered. These were deposited in short irregular rows, separately or in groups of twos and threes, in crevices in the upper surface of the bark. They were spherical—as round and smooth and shiny as pale-yellow pool balls. Their size I cannot accurately convey to you. Suffice to say that small specks of dust would be a fair comparison and I would never have been able to locate them without a microscope, yet within each of those minute glistening balls lay imprisoned a living germ, those marvelous chromosomes and genes, adequate food materials, and the whole inheritance of an amazing little race. It would have required countless thousands of these eggs to cover the palm of my hand. I could annihilate as many collembolans, were these eggs placed there, as men were wiped out in any major war. Such are our relative worlds.

The eggs were so smooth of shell they would have been in danger of rolling about or of being blown away, but for a wonderful thing which now happened. Within a short time little points or teats appeared at various places upon each egg, and from each of these projections a delicate hairline process grew rapidly outward. Some were straight, others slightly curved or wavy. They reached hither and yon, finally anchoring themselves at various points on the bark and at the sides of little crevices, tightening gradually and thus pulling the eggs into distorted shapes. Some eggs appeared faceted, others were pulled out at one side or at two or three places, while still others became suspended in mid-air between a network of these threads. (Figure 12.)

Could this be a remarkable example of symbiosis (a mutually beneficial relationship) between a mold and an insect's eggs? It seemed indeed possible that this was a growth of mold, but these eggs were developing embryos within, and mold would have indicated that they were dead. Perhaps living eggs can support a mold, I do not know, but whatever these threads which developed were, they did moor each egg securely until the young emerged six days later.

A sure sign that emergence was at hand was the appearance of brownish eye spots which could be seen through the shell of each egg. Collembolan eggs split apart. Instead of crawling forth through a more or less round hole eaten in the shell as many young caterpillars do, young springtails back out through the split a little at a time, waving their catapults from side to side, and each partial emergence alternating with a period of rest. They are weak at this time and their legs are partly folded, but within a short time they are walking about, feeding themselves, folding in and cleaning their antennae with their mouths, and acting like their parents generally. A newborn collembolan of this species is about as long as the first and second joints of its mother's antennae. Although almost exactly like Mama or Papa it still has a pudgy immature sort of air which at once spells baby, and like all things very young it is powerfully appealing. Completely independent from birth, my confined springtails grew to maturity quickly, and in the little glassine-topped box they carried on for months, feeding, courting, breeding, dying, and revealing through my microscope many secrets of their natural habits.

Entomologists consider the springtails to be among the most primitive of all insects. Their fossil forms are found imbedded in amber, a product once the gum of Tertiary trees which lived millions of years ago. Ants and flies, which are much more highly organized and advanced insects, are also found in amber, a fact which indicates how very old these collembolans as a group must be. Primitive and lowly as their position seems, they nevertheless back out of their eggs endowed with all of their faculties, ready to challenge the world and take full care of themselves, something which the young of no ape or human being can even begin to simulate, for the babies of primates are perhaps the most helpless of all.

The food habits of collembolans vary widely. The usual method followed by my bark-dwellers was to browse along

the furrows, where they could be seen pulling off and munch-
ing the minutest mouthfuls of algae and wood. Whether they
actually sought wood cells, or simply took them automatically
with the algae and later expelled them, I do not know. Cellulose compounds derived from sugars, and lignin, a complex phenolic substance, seem to be hard to digest. If springtails do eat wood, they may very possibly have protozoans
living within them to aid in the process, as termites do.

More interesting to me was the fact that my charges were
sometimes cannibalistic. With startled fascination I watched
the details of one such primitive feast through my three-
dimensional erecting microscope, as one collembolan discovered another which had just died. Immediately the living
one set about to devour the antennae and all six legs of its
succulent brother, as we might first relish the crisp legs of a
fried soft-shelled crab. Deliberately, the cannibal chewed
and sipped at the dead one's appendages, and as I watched,
consumed them one by one, pulling each in to its mouth with
one of its own legs, and occasionally stopping to lap or suck
up tiny dropped portions, just as a dog licks up the crumbs
from time to time when eating. I was surprised, for up
until this time I had looked upon these creatures as rather
kindly browsers like cows. The most interesting part of the
cannibalistic process was to witness the bitten-off fragments
of the dead insects sliding down through the neck passage
of the other, and to follow their course into the food canal
of a living body, somewhat like watching refuse going down
a drain. My powerful micro-lamp and the thin skin of the
collembolan made all of this possible, a ringside view of the
ingestion of one creature's lifeblood and substance into another, a rather gruesome transfusion perhaps, but a splendid
illustration of natural conservation.

Through the skin along the top of the living one's abdomen I also discerned slow dark waves, pulsations of a primi-

tive heartlike organ sluggishly agitating the transparent blood which bathed the whole interior of this animated organism without the need of arteries or veins or the myriad capillaries required by the higher, red-blooded animals.

I was struck by the almost mammallike actions of my collembolans: their deliberate manner when pulling food forward and toward their mouths with their "paws," their nosing about for dropped scraps and particles, and their apparent sniffing, doglike recognition of one another when two of them met on their wanderings. Peering through this wonderful binocular, my normal world was forgotten again and again, and I seemed to be actually living down there in their habitat with these queer beasts which were contemporaries and my equal in size. After months of observing my charges their world seemed as natural to me as my own back wood lot so familiar had it become, and even though it was inhabited, as we shall presently see, by many other grotesque creatures besides the springtails.

If a tiny area of bark such as this within my live-box—a two-by-two-inch fragment taken from a medium-sized oak tree—was capable of yielding the amazing fauna which I eventually discovered, what, I thought, might I not find for instance, upon a single *square foot* of a giant redwood or Sequoia? Wherever I have gone I have found absorbing associations of living things—at home, on isolated islands, in deciduous woods, in tropical rain forests, even in the desert of Arizona—and although I have yet to experience the excitement of observing the minutiae of a Sequoia or redwood grove, I am certain that there would be revealed groups of strange and perhaps even unnamed organisms which have evolved as remarkably through the centuries as the giants upon which they probably may be found.

Time and again new creatures appeared as I watched the bark through the microscope, and a drop or two of water added every other day seemed to be all that was needed to keep this little world thriving. There were flat-bodied little things called Corrodentia, and at least five kinds of microscopic mites, which are eight-legged creatures belonging to the order Acarina. (Figure 12.) One was oval and bottle green, with an almost luminous stripe down the center of its back. It reminded me at once of a highly polished gem, its stripe glowing like a ray within a fine star sapphire. These mites were so small that when running upon their short, fast-moving legs they often passed right under the motionless standing two-millimeter-long collembolans without the insects even being aware of them.

Another of the mites, even smaller than this oval gem, possessed a rounded brown body surmounted with the tiniest pimple for a head. It moved about in a more leisurely fashion, a casual but determined creature of whose business in the world I can tell you nothing whatever.

The third species was smaller still, but otherwise similar to the brown one above, while the fourth and strangest-looking of the lot I named the "mold-thread mite." Pinpoint in size and invisible to the naked eye, this object dwelt among the threads of mold which grew within the moist bark caverns in crevices. (Figure 12.) Slower of gait than any snail which ever lived, it dragged one hairlike leg after the other in the weariest and most tedious manner imaginable, making scarcely any progress at all, and so coated with adhering mold tangled in its own barely distinguishable hairs that it was only after long searching that by chance it was singled out from its environment.

But now hear this! Another mite—let us simply call it number five—came upon the scene in company with number four. Round of body, bright orange in color, and so minute that again it was merely by chance that I saw it at all, this inexplicable entity rode about nonchalantly clinging to the tip of a single hair of its already microscopic host. Here again was another denizen of the bark world about whose life history and purpose I could not even guess. What an amazing world it continues to be once you start investigating it.

From some deep crevice in the bark a tiny masterpiece of insect design crawled forth three weeks after I had started this menagerie. This was a lace-insect belonging to the family Tingididae, insignificant-looking to the naked eye, but actually one of the world's most surprising objects when magnified. Here was a six-legged creature with a flat head and body, but overlaying all of its standard insect equipment, even the lower-power lenses revealed an elaborate "solarium," a combined roof and shield studded with chitinous bubbles and windows and blisters, a sort of living marquee of translucent and delicate lace.

Using a set of higher-power lenses to examine the most prominent feature of this shield, I found that it consisted of a bean-shaped bulge or blister which was transparent, and glazed with many odd shaped bits of chitin, like the separate pieces in a window of leaded glass. I wondered what the purpose of such an elaborate design might serve, and again what this particular blister could be for. Was it for cushioning the creature's head? Was it filled with gas and thus functional in some subtle manner? Was it merely a useless decoration or simply another experiment within an experiment to be added to the millions which nature has invented?

I do not believe any of these suggestions explain the case. The creatures remain over the winter in bark crevices. In summer we find their eggs on the undersides of basswood leaves, and gregarious herds of young are then seen feeding and sometimes causing a skeletonized appearance of the foliage. This looks somewhat like the lacy coverings of the herds' growing bodies and may afford some protection, but the true purpose of the adult lace-insect's wonderful overcoat remains as another of those exquisite and baffling puzzles concerning living things. It was with profound respect that I tried to draw this creature's likeness. By peering alternately into my instrument and drawing laboriously, correcting a line here, a cell there, I gradually evolved fairly accurate and greatly enlarged pictures of them. (Figure 13.)

Getting back once more to our collembolans, we find that they have their enemies like all other living things. They are devoured by vicious little rove beetles which are slim creatures with short, square, folding wing covers like the doors of a cabinet, and under which their delicate flying wings are folded. I have watched these ravenous ones, these little gourmets sating themselves upon soft collembolan bodies, which they take into their mouths without benefit of their "hands" or appendages and consume bit by bit after the manner of a human youngster mouthing a marshmallow banana. There are small reddish-brown ants which kill and carry off the blue-and-violet springtails also, despite their gaudy colors, which tend to emphasize their presence against the green moss upon which they often live, rather than protecting them as "warning signals" to predators.

Young brook trout sometimes consume a surface-living species of collembolan * in enormous numbers,[2] but of all the known enemies of these creatures, I believe I discovered the most interesting in the heavy rain forest of British Guiana. This was a very minute species of predacious solitary wasp. Its whole life history is a story well worth telling, for it embodies a most unusual ecological association between these tiny wasps and the vast numbers of collembolans which inhabit the forest floor. I do not believe that the Peckhams or even J. H. Fabre ever had the good fortune to observe the life of an insect so intriguing.

* *Isotomurus palustris.*

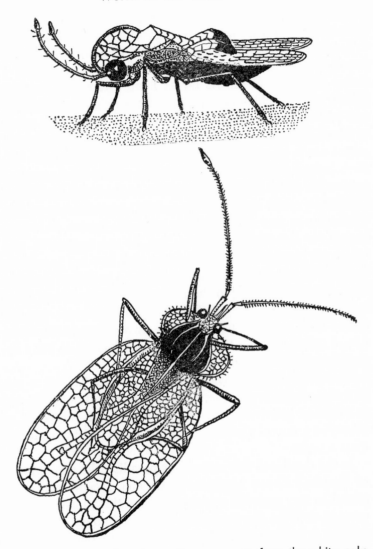

Figure 13. Top: The lace bug with a marquee from the white oaks. Enlarged fifteen times. *Bottom:* Another species whose young feed on basswood. (Approximate sketches)

Among the great moras and purplehearts and all the great trees of the Guianas, some towering a hundred and thirty feet in height, trees from which a single nut in some cases would dwarf thousands of the tiny insects, it is a wonder that I found this wasp at all. As far as I am aware, the smallest known species which constructs and provisions a distinctive and perfect little nest in which to raise its young, this speck of life challenges the tropical forest and jungle, and succeeds where much greater and more powerful animals might fail. Here indeed was an insect personality whose habits were as new to me when first I studied them as the wasp itself. This Lilliputian went about her household requirements as methodically as any comparatively gigantic hornet or honeybee. Up to this time some years ago, no one apparently had taken the trouble to study or name her, but my specimens being new, the insect is now known by a technical designation rather frightening to the layman.* Twenty-two of these wasps without touching could rest upon the twenty-two letters of their scientific name; for my own convenience, therefore, I called her the tiny purse wasp which is at once descriptive of herself and her nest.

We are dealing here with a *solitary* species. That is to say, an insect which lives alone, builds her nest without help, and in addition provisions her young with food. There is no colony or group of workers, and after a very brief mating, not even a male.

In the depths of this naturalist's paradise, the actual locale of Hudson's *Green Mansions* in Guiana, I came across the purselike tiny nest. All woven of golden thread, she had suspended it from the underside of a big green leaf which formed a landing platform and roof all in one, and as an occasional shaft of sunlight found its way down through the foliage above and struck the leaf, the suspended cradle was

---

* *Microstigmus guianensis* Rowh. New species.[3]

outlined in an emerald chlorophyll glow. Bobbing at the end of a woven gossamerlike stem in the moist, plant-scented air, it touched my face and thus came the discovery.

Come with me now to an observation post in the rain forest, a high magnificent forest whose shaded isles are the home of jaguar and ocelot, of agouti and peccary, of tapir and tyra, of ant trushes and tinamou, of driver ants and huge blue butterflies, a forest in whose canopy dwell red howlers and spider monkeys, beesas and sloths, toucans and parrots, cotingas and tanagers, hummingbirds and harpy eagles, and a host of other wonderful creatures. In such company *Microstigmus* raises her progeny.

The wasp is all but invisible upon her nest because of her size and blending colors, but through a magnifying glass she is an attractive yellow, with dotted crown and compound eyes of the brightest green. Her independence seems exaggerated by her enormous surroundings; actually she comes and goes heedless both of me and the great forest. We wonder how this minute thing first learned to weave so perfect an abode for her offspring, a nest as elaborate in detail and engineering skill as those forty-two-inch creations of the oropéndola birds of Panama.° With wonder we watch this all but microscopic cog in the great wheel of forest life, absorbed in the task of perpetuating her race in a habitat which for such little organisms would seem rife with dangers.

Perhaps the secret of her success lies in her minuteness. Perhaps she fits, one might say, into the niches of many of the surrounding hazards. Should a great hard fruit pod or branch fall toward her, its preceding air currents would simply brush her to one side. Were she hunting upon the ground, even my huge foot would simply press her into a tiny cavity or niche unharmed. She may even be overlooked by predators, a possibility suggested by abundant nests, and the

° See Chapter 10, Part 4.

small numbers of young which the wasps raise in each of them. Few young indicate few enemies, low mortality.

Several feet below the typical nest which we are observing lies the forest floor, always wet and cushionlike underfoot, a deep brown disintegrating blanket of fallen leaves and seeds, of twigs and molding branches, of fungi and bacteria, and the dank waste matter of animal life. Still below this epidermis of dead, but not yet completely decomposed material and its attendant living things, lies the world of the humus sheltering an association of organisms quite different from those in the strata above. In these layers live the jungle types of our now familiar collembolans, some in honey-colored costumes, others in gray and lavender and gun metal, in black and glistening brown.

Upon them our tiny purse wasp preys, not for herself, for she feeds only upon nectar, but for her larval offspring. Here then we have two extremes in insect life bound up in the closest association. The wasp belongs to the order Hymenoptera, the highest and most specialized insect order of all, while the collembolans, as stated before, are at the bottom of the classification heap, simple, primitive structurally, wingless, and probably little changed from ancient ancestors which jumped about in the dim geological past. The two insects are intimately associated in life, but upon opposite sides of a canyon morphologically.

Making journey after journey from forest floor to nest, the wasp carries in many collembolan victims. Whether she stings each one, as most of the larger solitary wasps sting their prey, I cannot say for sure. In any case, the springtails remain motionless as if paralyzed, plump and fresh, just where she places them in rounded masses packed in the two to six pockets into which the bottoms of these nurseries are divided. Upon each food mass a single elongated white egg is now deposited, a potential *Microstigmus* resting upon its ball of collembolan sardines.

Here ended my initial observations in the forest locale. It seemed a pity, but it was much more convenient to clip the leaf with the nest and carry them to the tent for further watching. Strange but true, in this case the little wasp came also. Undismayed, she had remained within the nest just as if nothing had happened, a fact which led to the discovery that apparently none of the cells or pockets are sealed up after they have been provisioned and the eggs deposited. None of the various nests examined later, on two trips to Guiana, contained sealed-off cells. The usual procedure among the majority of solitary species is to seal each provisioned cell with its single egg, after which the parent has nothing more to do with it. In the tiny purse wasp we have a solitary species which nevertheless remains on guard within the nest while the offspring feed themselves, a sort of evolutionary intermediate between the typical solitary Hymenoptera and the social species which take full care of the feeding process from day to day during the life of the larvae.

The egg of *Microstigmus* hatches in three days, and the newborn larva is a whitish, footless grub which sets to work at once upon the stored collembolan food mass, consuming it completely in about one week. Then, somewhat after the manner of a human being gorged with a Thanksgiving dinner, the larva sinks into a blissful state of torpor, but in this case while wonderful processes gradually transform it, in about three weeks, into the third condition called the pupa. So transformed again, into a glasslike yellowish and folded adult, *Microstigmus* lies motionless for several more days before the miracle of color, emergence and flight, and true adulthood, the goal of every living thing is realized.

In contemplating this life history we should recognize the fact that here within the typical wasp larva something profound transpires which turns the helpless, defenseless baglike object into the finished and beautiful creature, with highly evolved internal organs, strong wings, compound eyes, keen sense organs, sting and poison glands and efficient organs of reproduction in two distinct sexes. It is almost as if we were witnessing a miraculous and complete revolution in the being, almost as if we had discovered two entirely different beings built at slightly different times from the identical materials, and it is a mystery why such radical life histories are necessary. We know that there is a considerable breakdown of the larval substances before the transformations to pupa and adult take place in the rebuilding process. This process is controlled by a tiny gland in the head called the corpus allatum, which lies just behind the insect brain. The amount of the hormone neotenin ("youth substance") secreted by this gland seems to be the controlling factor in the stages of the metamorphosis. Witnessing such transformations as these, in all wasps, butterflies, beetles, and many other kinds of insects, has a sobering effect upon our human conceit, an effect which quickly reduces us to a humbler and more respectful level in the face of nature's inventions.

During eleven months spent in the forests of British Guiana at different times, I found three distinct types of nests made by these little *Microstigmus* insects, all of which were within a small radius of our two research areas, one at Kalacoon on the Mazaruni and the other at Kartabo on the Cuyuni River. These nests, differing in the materials of their construction and in the forms of their suspending stems, point to the presence of at least three distinct species in this part of British Guiana. Here, then, is a very interesting field of investigation for someone with patience and a love for the tropical forests.

The commonest nests were those made by the species described in this chapter. These were suspended by short stems, which like the nests proper were woven of a delicate golden-yellow or golden-brown silklike fiber or hair, which it occurred to me might possibly have been stolen from caterpillars or their cocoons, especially after I had examined it under the microscope.

The second type were similar in shape to those just described, but their greenish-gray walls when viewed under the microscope were seen to be made of minute shinglelike fragments which seemed to be bits of lichen. The nests were suspended from the undersides of leaves by short spiral stems resembling little coiled springs. The third and most interesting type were constructed of very minute wood chips, some gray, some brown, and overlaid here and there with what I judged to be lichen fragments, apparently fastened on with silk. In shape they reminded me strongly of the baglike nests of certain South American flycatchers or those beautiful ones created by the California bush tit, but in this case, of course, in extreme miniature, and it struck me as an extraordinary thing that two such widely separated creatures as a bird and a wasp should have hit upon the same architectural plan. The most amazing thing about these tiny nests were their stems which were like threads several inches in length, coated with bits of wood and lichen fragments, thus each nest bobbed and careened in every forest breeze. The baglike nursery ends of these swinging nests measured but three-eighths of an inch in length (Figure 14.)

Before passing, in the chapters which follow, to other engrossing corridors of life, let us stop and visualize in the mind's eye three imaginary scenes. First a nebula such as Cygnus, a concept of uncountable stars, a space continent made up of billions of suns and possible planetary systems far too vast for our complete comprehension. Next in your imagination stand before one of the thousand-year-old Sequoias,

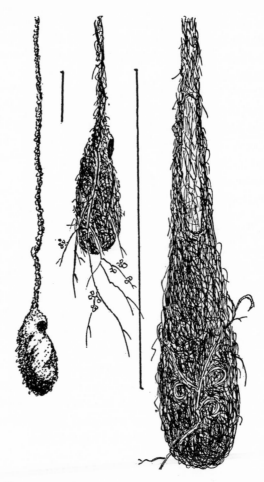

Figure 14. The same architectural plan is hit upon by insects and birds. *Left to right:* South American *Microstigmus* wasp, California bush tit, Oropéndola oriole. Total lengths of nests and stems: 4 inches, 12 inches, 42 inches.

an aggregation of tiny cells, as uncountable as the stars in the nebula, which have erected with unerring perfection the magnificent dwarfing organism which is this tree. Last, but not least in interest, visualize once more the bark world of the collembolans as I have tried to describe it in part of this chapter.

These three scenes are as different physically as any three could be, but the perfection to be observed in each one, the orderly wholes into which they have evolved, and which even with our limited senses we may perceive, offers comforting evidence of the attention which has been lavished upon the tiniest living things as well as the greatest objects in the universe.

Such things rudely crowd the skeptic of a system, an impetus, and a guiding law behind it all. Is there, I wonder, a civilized human being who in the real depths of his or her being sincerely believes that even such as we have encountered and studied so far in this book could be but the work of drunken stagehands pulling the scenic ropes of evolution at random?

CHAPTER 6

Of Tastes and Odors

A CERTAIN flower bed at our place in Connecticut I call the "luring bed." Rich in nectar offerings, seductive with its odors, its plants and flowers lure hummingbirds in numbers, and insects by the thousands. Experience has taught me to keep this bed very simple, but to fertilize it richly, to mulch it before winter, and to plant it year after year with but two annuals, beneath the two perennials which constitute the other half of my efficient attracting quartet.

Tallest of these are the perennial butterfly bushes, white, deep pink, and magenta buddleias which really live up to their entomological name. Below them grow petunias in many hues and forms, and through their varied ranks rise fiery salvias and the tall spikes of wild loosestrife with their hundreds of reddish-purple blooms. This is all there is to my "luring bed," so let us take a closer look at these flowers which bring so many welcome visitors.

Each lilaclike spire of a butterfly bush is a closely packed mass of tiny separate flowerlets, housing within their little tubes droplets of the sweetest natural fluid. Butterflies come from far and near to regale themselves here in lavish drinking bouts, and so short are these flower tubes that even the smallest of the eager imbibers need uncoil but half its watch-spring tongue to obtain the nectar. Here come red admirals, and monarchs, spotted purples and fritillaries, blues and swallowtails, painted ladies and pierids, and darting skippers seeking their mates as well as sweets. At dusk the clearwing moths, long tongues extended, drift up and down like hummingbirds before the spires. At night come many smaller moths, and in the full sun of summer days a host of bees and wasps and flower-flies know that these short-throated blossoms will not repel their shorter tongues.

Much deeper nectar lies within the tube-throats of the petunias where it is also sought at night by moths. No flowers have a more compelling, ethereal odor, launched perhaps from complex mingled esters. Into the depths of the fiery *Salvia* blossoms crawl myriads of tiny black bees and many other insects, responding to a scent so delicate that it all but escapes our far less receptive senses. The larger bees visit them less often, but hummingbirds find them a certain lure. Throughout the blooming summer period a bed of these flowers will attract them, and sometimes for at least a part of the hummingbird population, migration may be delayed by these tall red spikes until much later than usual.

If red flowers are not visited by honeybees, as some naturalists claim, the author is puzzled by those which *are* attracted to deep-pink and almost-red gladioli in other parts of the garden, and why so many smaller bees love the salvias. Stranger yet seems the claim that the honeybee is color-blind to red, and that its "inability" to see this color is the reason for the "rareness" of exclusively red flowers.[1] Rareness indeed! What of the fire pink and the wild bright-red columbine? What of the cardinal flower's glowing brookside petals, or the bee balm and scarlet-painted cup, and the trumpet creeper? What of the passion vine and cardinal climber, the coral honeysuckle, the scarlet runner and the species in my luring bed? There are plenty of bees which *can* see red, and there are red flowers thriving all around us.

Let us now taste flower nectar as the bees find it. To do this, break off a petunia blossom or a flowerlet of *Buddleia.* Next, very carefully sever the base of the floral tube and place the longer end between the lips. Now apply gentle suction, and if you are lucky you may receive ever so delicate a portion of the flower's glandular offering. If you cannot master the technique with these rather difficult subjects, try the easier white-and-yellow tubes of the common honeysuckle, for this delicious substance secreted regularly and plentifully by flowering organisms in general is perhaps most lavishly secreted within the honeysuckle's narrow throats. Test the nectar tubes of this abundant vine by breaking off their narrowest ends with your fingers and then slowly drawing out their pistils still attached to the severed bases. The pistils will act as miniature pistons, each forcing a glistening droplet of nectar into view, and which, like the gods, you may then imbibe and enjoy. (Figure 15.) Remember that this clear liquid found in flowers *is not honey.* It is nectar which may only be transformed into honey by unknown chemical processes which take place within the body of the bee. Nectars from a large number of different flowers taste very much the same, at least to the author, but their chemistry may vary considerably, for as everyone knows, honey is found in dozens of shades and flavors.

The loosestrife bushes of our "luring bed" were transplanted from a bit of swampy ground in Connecticut near the author's home. They belonged to the identical European species which Darwin studied so intently, and which upon being introduced into the United States became very common indeed.* Strange as it may seem to those who understand, or believe they understand, ecology wherein it relates to plants and soil, my *Lythrum* bushes grew splendidly in dry

* *Lythrum salicaria.* Whole swamps are often magenta with this flower.

sandy soil, which, although well watered, was radically different from that of its original habitat. Why we never find
even a few of them sprouting unaided—from some of the
millions of minute seeds which are annually produced—anywhere away from swampy ground, and thriving as mine have,
no one has yet explained. My successful bushes are highly
prized, not only for their great beauty, but because I now
have the species with which Darwin made one of his classic
discoveries, right where I may observe them myself.

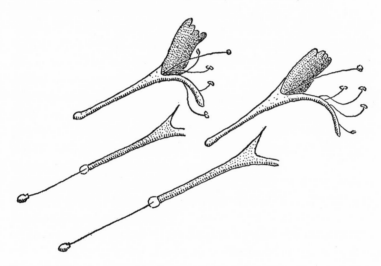

Figure 15. Two honeysuckle flowers. *Below:* The pistils drawn out extracting large drops of nectar.

Of all the plants in my "luring bed," loosestrife is of greatest interest from the biologist's point of view because the
flowers are found in three kinds upon a single bush. The
pistils of these flowers occur in three different lengths also,
and in each of these flower forms there are two sets of stamens differing in size and function. In addition, and in keeping with such a remarkable setup, pollen of different sizes

and of two different colors—yellow and green—are produced by these male organs.

It would seem therefore, that there should be eighteen ways in which pollination might take place when insects transferred the two kinds (colors) of pollen to the stigmas upon the different length pistils or female organs. But Darwin proved by long experiment that only pollen transferred in certain ways, from certain stamens to certain pistils, would insure fertilization. Here in this common plant we have one of the most intricate "marriage" mechanisms which has ever been evolved by nature. To quote Darwin himself: "Altogether this one species includes three females or female organs and three sets of male organs, and as distinct from one another as if they belonged to different species; and if smaller functional differences are considered, there are five different sets of males. Two of the three hermaphrodites * must coexist, and pollen must be carried by insects reciprocally from one to the other, in order that either of the two should be fully fertile; but unless all three forms coexist, two sets of stamens will be wasted, and the organization of the species, as a whole, will be incomplete. On the other hand, when all three hermaphrodites coexist, and pollen is carried from one to the other, the scheme is perfect; there is no waste of pollen and no false coadaptation. In short, nature has ordained a most complex marriage arrangement, namely a triple union between hermaphrodites—each hermaphrodite being in its female organ quite distinct from the other two hermaphrodites and partially distinct in its male organs, and each furnished with two sets of males." [2]

It will pay anyone who appreciates the perfection to be found in natural associations to watch closely the insect pollinators intent upon their business at the mouths of the loose-

* Individuals (flowers in this case) having both male and female reproductive organs.

strife blossoms. It is not a haphazard method which each one follows, and each species seems to have its special approach. With bumblebees the proper pollen seems to adhere in greatest abundance to the parts of the insects which will next come in contact with the proper parts of the next flower visited. Leaf-cutter bees have a different approach altogether. One flower-fly sails directly in to each pistil after only brushing the stamens, while still another very odd one comes with half of its long, wirelike body bent down almost at right angles to the rest of its abdomen. At the loosestrife one becomes lost in a fascinating specialized world.

Observing the various insects which so delight in the four flowers named, apparently in preference to all others near by, I became convinced that it was neither color nor nectar itself which lured them to the bed, but rather the sweet, the odd, the almost disturbing, or even imperceptible (to human beings) scents which these blossoms cast collectively upon the air—often subtle creations from the hidden glands of these organisms.

Experimenting with various sweet substances during the zenith of the flight periods, these trials seemed to demonstrate that man-made materials such as glycerin and saccharin, which are enormously sweet to our sense of taste, are not in the least attractive to insects even when pleasantly diluted. In weak solutions such as I used, neither of these compounds could be harmful even to the most delicate sipper, but no insects favored them with a visit as far as I could tell, and both solutions were *odorless* from our point of view.

Saccharin, whose chemical formula is $C_6H_4COSO_2NH$, is *five hundred times* sweeter than ordinary sugar or saccharose, which has the somewhat simpler formula $C_{12}H_{22}O_{11}$. The formula of glycerin, a very sweet, warm-tasting compound reads $C_3H_5(OH)_3$, while the sugar of honey, inexplicably manufactured by the bees from nectar, is actually dextrose, which is chemically written $C_6H_{12}O_6$. In the event you have forgotten the fundamentals of chemistry let it be said that in these formulas C stands for carbon, H for hydrogen, O for oxygen, S for sulphur, and N for nitrogen, while the numerals indicate the number of atoms of each element present in the molecule of the substance.

Insects of course care nothing for chemistry or any of this human jargon, but the fact that they are attracted to some of these things and not to others, although all are compounds composed of a very few common elements so combined as to add up to what *we* consider sweet, indicates after all how ignorant we actually are about the sensations and reactions which food and other substances produce in other creatures. In the case of my luring flowers, their special scents are, I believe, always picked up by the insects. So also the odors of honey and sugar bring a few to sample them, yet very few kinds indeed. It even may be true that such things as saccharin and glycerin send forth chemical messages which repel the six-footed creatures. We do not know.

I have found by experiment that when pure honey is exposed in open dishes, few insects other than honeybees and a scattering of ants are attracted to it. Solutions of refined sugar and water also usually remain unattended by all but a few ants which stumble upon them and then carry the news of the find back to their fellows, but a brown sugar and water mixture with its distinctive stronger odor brings many more species and individuals. Add rum and stale beer to this stuff, brush it upon the trunks of woodland trees of a hot summer dusk in Connecticut, and you will attract some of the most beautifully colored large moths you have ever set eyes upon. Many smaller species, as well as ants and beetles and roaches, will also partake of this odoriferous lure, while butterflies, bees, wasps, and hornets will arrive to lap it up by day. Yet such mixtures do not always work. Strangely enough, similar experiments with various boozy-sweet potions in tropical forests rich in insect life gave very disappointing and meager results. In British Guiana nothing came to my well-sugared trees along the jungle trails except a few small beetles, while in the heavily forested mountains of Dominica, where fine big moths abound, only centipedes and huge crickets seemed to appreciate my most intoxicating concoctions.

The more I experimented at home and in the south, the more confusing matters became, for I soon found that odors which we consider disgusting and repulsive were extremely alluring to some of our most beautiful butterflies, which are normally clean feeders upon nectar. A dead snake, a pile of excrement, a puddle of horse urine, fermenting saps—all may become popular brothels to be fought over by their insect patrons. Still other insects such as the beautiful *Catocala* moths (of which more in Chapter 8) become fit subjects for the AA, for in dozens they come to the horrible rum and sugar mixtures already mentioned, and upon these vile potions they become so thoroughly inebriated that sometimes they may be collected by hand.

In Colombia, South America, the smell of the sweat of our pack horses and burrows attracted long-tailed blue-tinged butterflies which lapped the fluid avidly. In the forest of Panama our own perspiration brought various insects, including small bees, *stingless,* but annoying as they sipped the salty liquid drops upon our foreheads; but most remarkable of all among the insects which delight in what is repelling to us are the *Necrophorus* and *Silpha* beetles, major-domos of the arthropod sanitary corps, whose definite collective function is to see that small birds and animal forms which die naturally are properly buried, and that their vital substances are conserved and quickly employed over again. Out of the millions of birds and mammals and reptiles and others which die annually, how many have you ever run across in the woods and fields and thickets? Very few to be sure, for almost as soon as any creature dies, its body sends forth messages which seem to be communicated to these beetles at once. Posthaste they respond and come humming through the air, to tumble suddenly and clumsily upon the lifeless object.

Here in the East these beetles may be black ones with two squarish, orange-red spots upon each wing-cover, or they may be larger ones marked with somewhat similar plain red areas. In addition to these there are also smaller oval beetles with yellow thoraxes, known as the silphas, and still others, on down the scale to tiny black insects which resemble fine glossy beads. The two large, brightly marked species mentioned above are the appropriately named *Necrophorus* beetles. They measure an inch or over in length, and although Lutz in his *Field Book of Insects* states that he has never seen them in the act of burying anything, the author has witnessed this interesting procedure many times.

When the beetles arrive upon the scene, they set to work at once to burrow beneath the dead creature. Then from below, they vigorously push the earth out to the sides with their powerful heads and legs, thus lowering the object into a neatly fitting grave, in which thereafter they consume its flesh and probably deposit their eggs. In my garden lay a dead scarlet tanager one day. It seemed to be quite fresh and its plumage was still brilliant, but already the message had gone out and a quartet of the beetle undertakers had arrived, and as I watched, the body heaved slightly sidewise. I ran for the motion-picture camera, set it up for a record, and within an hour nothing but the tanager's head remained visible. A short time afterward the entire body of the bird had vanished into the earth. Some years before, I recorded the case of a house wren which was completely buried by a number of these insects working in unison, in eight minutes, a feat which I do not expect to see equaled again. In the heavy rain forests of British Guiana I have also often watched the scavenger beetles at work, where they arrive almost at once upon anything which has been killed, or upon excrement, but here, perhaps as a reward for their gruesome tasks, they are gorgeous creatures clothed in shining ruby armor. Although these things may seem unpleasant to talk about, we must realize that here again we are observing something very important which has been attended to by nature and the great force which understood conservation millions of years before man did.

If, as we feel certain, the world which we perceive is not at all like that which the insects experience, it is anthropomorphic even to imagine that foods taste the same to them as they do to us. We are, indeed, quite ignorant of how anything tastes to them; neither can we say how flowers or honey or any other substance actually affects their senses, and they may not be capable of experiencing sweetness or sourness as we do at all, and all of our experiments may therefore be a waste of time.

Where odors are concerned, it is interesting to remember that *we* have sensory cells equipped with hairs within our nasal cavities which are distinct from the coarse filtering hairs in our nostrils,[3] and that insects have sensory hairs situated upon their antennae, sometimes in great profusion, but who can say whether or not these creatures and human beings employ these hairs in a similar manner, or whether or not both are signaled with the same messages by such things as the perfume of petunias and the odor of carrion?

And what, after all, is sweetness or sourness, bitterness or fetidness anyway? Sourness seems invariably to indicate the presence of an acid, but, as we cannot readily define these other sensations or say for sure that any lower forms of life are cognizant of them as we are, let us play with the words for a minute.

Webster tells us that sweet may refer to a large number of things. We may have something that simply smells good, or anything opposed to sourness, or things arising from graciousness or sympathy; things that are simply not salty such as water or fresh butter, or one's own sweet self; "sweet assaults upon credulity" (which this is rapidly becoming), or freedom from noxious gases, or staleness, putrescence, harshness, or unmelodiousness. Or, in other words, sweet really seems to mean pleasing or agreeable in most any way, but only to human beings, for if such ideas and conditions were correct from all viewpoints, then we would be forced to admit that carrion and such are sweet, for these things are exceedingly pleasing to many mammals other than human ones, to some of the birds, to beetles and butterflies and many other forms of animal life.

CHAPTER 7

A.M. in the Wood Lot

THE curtain rises. It is a soft and fragrant dawn in Connecticut and the month is May. From a dead twig upon a black alder bush almost in front of my nose, infinitely tiny mist drops have outlined a spider's web in silvery white. The web is four inches wide at its base and it is constructed in the form of a somewhat elongated triangle as though it were made of three little ladders, side by side, whose rungs are the cross threads of the snare. Altogether it reminds me of a ship's mast ladder in triplicate, and near its apex, clinging to a long taut guy wire of silk is the clever spinner herself, who by alternately pulling taut and letting go this device snaps the whole trap, so to speak, into the bodies or wings of blundering flying insects.

Remarkable as this trick of the triangle spider * may seem, we have no idea of how it may have originated. It is not her web, however, but a cluster of glistening eggs which remind us, once more, that like all of the other living things which we have been observing, each of the earth's countless spiders is also endowed with that irresistible urge—reproduction. Of this universal drive in animals, the new-laid egg mass is again the symbol.

The spider people, low in the scale of life as we like to be-

* *Hyptiotes cavatus.*

99

lieve we understand it, nevertheless enact in their courtships scenes and episodes which are among the most curious in nature. They amaze us in their insistence upon linking ceremony with the mating act, pursuits unconsciously followed which bring sexual fulfillment in a manner which is unique.

Spiders belong to that huge class called the Arachnida. They seem to have been singled out from uncountable species of arthropods—crustaceans, centipedes, scorpions, and insects, and in fact, from all of the other jointed-foot creatures which constitute this great phylum—for a radical sexual experiment which sets them apart, as far as I am aware, from all others.

Situated upon the heads of these eight-legged creatures, there are short, somewhat leglike appendages, the second pair of which are the pedipalps, one on either side of the mouth parts. Their segments nearest to the head are called the coxae and endites, while the remaining ones constitute the palpus. In view of their position, in male spiders the palpi have been modified into the most singular organs imaginable. Differing in their shapes and intricate construction, they are employed in the *transference of the spermatozoa* to the reproductive organs of the females.

On the underside of the male's abdomen, in a furrow near its base, lies the external opening of his reproductive organs. Before mating takes place, however, there is an important and delicate ritual to be attended to, and with the greatest of care he spins what I call the "initiation web." It is a beautiful, shining, miniature mat, a silken bed actually, spun of the finest gossamer, and upon this soft creation of his ardor he now ejects a drop of the precious seminal fluid. This living substance, swarming as in other animals, including man, with myriad microscopic, tail-lashing sperm cells, he now draws up into the swollen ends of his palpi, as we might pull a liquid up into a rubber-bulbed syringe. Here he retains this rich manna of inheritance, until the female, gradually influenced by his courtship gestures, by his dances and wig-wagging, or by his alternate retreats and advances, at length allows embrace and the transfer of the sperm from the palpi to the folds of her now receptive organs.

This strange innovation has eliminated the necessity of a male primary intromittent organ altogether. In place of the sexual act, so simple and satisfactory in the case of most of the higher animals, we find in the spiders this complicated arrangement wherein specialized and variously shaped injectors have been evolved to fit into equally specialized orifices of the female, which are sometimes ridged and grooved or otherwise molded in order to match only the induction apparatus of the male of the species. Astonishing in its radical differences, we are here face to face with a vastly interesting experiment whose advantages or actual reason we cannot discern. It is one of those great puzzles, met with again and again all along the highways of natural history. (Figure 16.)

Behind the hill and the woods and the spangled spider's web, the sun is now rising, the air grows warmer and the day brighter. Little by little its rays dapple and bathe the surfaces of thousands of young leaves, whose chlorophyll strains exquisite green from the spectrum and reflects it to my delighted eyes. With the sun has come a chorus which saturates the woods, sounds which no human words or phrases may describe, and for this pleasure of listening again, a pleasure which never diminishes, I have waited expectantly in the woodland here since half past three. One after another, as the songs issue from the night roosts of thrushes and grosbeaks, of wrens and vireos and warblers, my recorder spins faithfully, miraculously preserving these stirring vibrations created and ejected by the little muscular contraptions, the

syringes, which are specialized modifications of the wind-
pipes of these sometimes highly emotional creatures which
we call birds. Later, in the dead of winter, when spring's
only reminders may be a disintegrating robin's nest in a pine,
or a tattered home of a vireo staring at me from among the

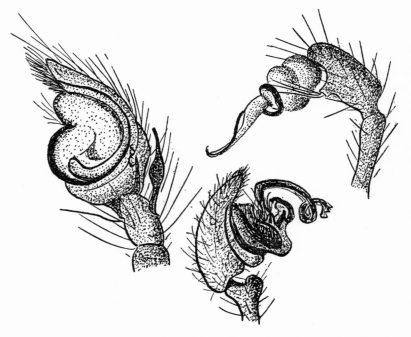

Figure 16. Sex organs of male spiders. Left to right: palpus of *Anyphaena
gracilis,* genital bulb of *Xysticus ferox,* palpus of *Hypochilus thorellii.*

very twigs and crotches which in June I combed in vain, the
miracle is repeated, for at any time I may bring back to my
starved ears the lush songs and memories of this very morning
in May.

On this particular day, however, this soft spring morning,
not all was happiness and song. Looking up, I saw what

seemed at first to be a curled dead leaf hanging from a tendril of a honeysuckle vine. Moving closer I saw that this was a dead ruby-throat, a hummingbird hanging head down and still gripping the tendril in its firmly locked feet. To this day, this tragic little body is on exhibition in the museum, for as astonishing as it may seem to many visitors, it is no secret to the bird student or the ornithologist that when a passerine bird goes to roost, a locking bone in each foot prevents its toes from relaxing their hold. Here was a hummingbird which never woke up; neither did its locking bones relax, and there the bird remained, dead, but fast to its perch. As the skin upon its feet atrophied and shrank, the tiny body fell head downward and thus I discovered it. There is a puzzle locked in these locking bones. How did they evolve when the primitive birds first left the ground for their somewhat safer aerial perches? Why were they necessary in birds but not in arboreal mammals? We do not know.

Although there are roads and homes close by, our woodland of less than an acre has been preserved through all the years. Huge silvery beeches with odd and angular branches spread their dark-green leaves in a dense canopy above a host of struggling offspring wherein chestnut-sided warblers just up from Panama and Guatemala sometimes stop to build their nests. Nearby stands a tall Liriodendron * with trunk of gray and twigs of sienna brown. Its splendid squarish, four-lobed leaves and its exquisite blossoms like wondrous aerial water lilies never fail to astonish me. All delicate yellows and greens, richly daubed with cadmium orange where the six long petals join the base, few stop to appreciate its perfection when this May-June bloomer is at its best. There is nothing more beautiful than the pastel shades of these

* *Liriodendron tulipifera*, the tulip tree.

great blossoms even in the tropical forests of Panama, Guiana, or Brazil.

Our woods are rich in oaks—the scarlet and the pin oaks, and the white oaks especially—with varied trunks and barks, with leaves of many shapes, and rich in aphid life and larvae; they are the pantries of migrating warblers.

In July the second-growth basswoods fill the grove with perfume as rich and moving as anything of the summer nights. Within the little yellowish blossoms, microscopic color-matching thrips hold vast excited sex conventions. Clinging by tiny claws and agitating hair-cluster wings which flash periodically like little living lighthouse beams, they strain forward, eagerly signaling offers of intercourse in their heavily perfumed cubicles.

In our woodland, spice bushes glow yellow also in the early spring, and black alders later load themselves with scarlet berries. There are birches and elms and sour gums, maples and ironwood trees, and occasional grapevines bending and twisting to the canopy of leaves above. Beneath these trees are shrubs and saplings striving toward the sun, and still closer to the woodland carpet dwell the various ferns, the wild geraniums and jacks and jewelweeds, the horse balms and spikenards and adder's tongues, the violets and the day flowers, and still below these, the mosses and liverworts in the realm of snails and slugs, of mites and springtails, of ants and beetles and termites, of myriapods and isopods.

Down in the dark humus itself, fungi, molds, and bacteria hold sway, while earthworms, and nematodes in myriads blindly thread their way through a medium abounding in enemies. Among these there is a subtle slayer-mold. Along its advancing threads as it grows, it extends microscopic three-celled rings, shaped like little life preservers, but whose function is to kill these creatures.* Entering a ring is always

* For more about nematodes, see page 61.

fatal to the nematode, for upon contact the three cells swell enormously, thus squeezing and holding the victim until the plant absorbs and digests it. No one knows how lowly molds evolved such devices or what controls the inflation of these efficient ring traps.

From a somewhat more distant position, or from the average unobservant point of view, the fragmentary picture which I have drawn, and which I have already taken five pages to outline, adds up to just—the woods.

In years gone by there were miles of climax forest thriving up and down these Connecticut hills and valleys. The swamps between them still survive, while boulders and rock debris carried for hundreds of miles by the glaciers now mantle the ground or dot the woods and open fields. There is a rock within our little woods which tells an amazing story. It arrived there no doubt thousands of years ago upon the back of a glacier. There it finally melted out, bearing scars and cracks from its violent contact with others near by. Now it is partly buried by the debris of ages. Earthworms cast their loads of lumpy waste and soil around it year after year, thus helping in its slow but certain interment. In one of the cracks a maple seed lodged not long ago and already a tree has grown which will one day, perhaps within our lifetime, split this stone. Thus, even in this half-acre woodland we see the age-old processes of new soil and new forest in the making before our eyes.

Somehow, as I have said, our fragment of the forest has survived. Now isolated like an island, it has become a miniature sanctuary for birds and many other forms of life, a tiny island of green, of food and shelter and underground water, which may possibly retain unchanged, even elements of its primeval self. Here come tropical birds to spend their summers right in our own back yard. These are the scarlet tanagers, the grosbeaks, the indigo buntings, the humming-

birds and thrushes, the flycatchers and redstarts, and sometimes other warblers. I call them tropical because they only
spend their nesting periods with us before hurrying back to
the rain forests and jungles. Sitting in a comfortable canvas
chair at the woodland's border or in a little clearing in its
center, I may observe, according to the season, one interesting
event after another, may watch the drama of life unfold—
migration and the intensity of courtship, the woes and joys
of territorialism, home-building and fighting for it, the quest
and killing of animal food, the stalking, interloping predator,
the depredations of thieves and murderers, and the trials of
launching offspring successfully or with tragedy into the
world, whether they be the young of lowly creatures or the
more selfish, greedy "by-products" of the amphibians and
reptiles, birds and mammals.

When the woods are lush in May, ground water seeping
from the hillside nearby trickles into hollows in the leaf-
carpeted land; there it stays perhaps for weeks, long enough
some years for amazing minutiae to populate these miniature
pools, but from whence they came in the very beginning, no
one knows. Two of these irregular arrivals are called cladoc-
erans and ostracods. The former are the water fleas or
Daphnia, although they are not insects in any sense of the
word. Both animals are actually minute crustaceans, so small
that they appear as mere darting specks within the water,
and even at that, one must look carefully to single out the
individuals. (Figure 1.)

Daphnia possess transparent bivalve shells which, however, are constructed as a single protective covering. They
have distinct and curiously beaked heads; a large compound
wreathlike eye, and often a smaller eye-spot situated in front
of the larger one. This big eye may be curiously and usefully
rotated by means of special muscles within the head, where
there is also a brain and an optic ganglion with many nerves

which lead to different parts of the body. Two sets of appendages protrude from the head also. The smaller pair bear sense rods or hairs, while the larger pair act as antennae and powerful oars, being jointed and beautifully branched and plumed in many species.

Daphnia feed upon the swarming cells of algae and diatoms and other microscopic organisms, grinding them in well-formed jaws, and they are important food items themselves for thousands of little fishes. They are hatched from eggs which are extremely resistant, and the females produce fertile eggs for long periods without contact with the males. These strange little animals, which are found in many shapes and sizes, are often so numerous in ponds that they cloud great areas of the water. They are among the most complex of all the tiny aquatic organisms living today.

The second kind of little animals which populate these early leaf pools, the ostracods, are enclosed in true bivalve shells of lime, so shaped that when closed the objects resemble minute beans. Viewed from the front, however, many are distinctly heart-shaped as will be seen in the sketch, Figure 1. These shells open upon a ligament hinge, and from the slit between them the creature's antennae and legs and swimming appendages protrude. They have well-formed mandibles, but on the whole they are much simpler organisms than the *Daphnia,* and lacking a heart, well-oxygenated water must of necessity be constantly circulated through the valves by respiratory screens attached to the mouth parts. Despite their simpler make-up, for some unfathomable reason their spermatozoa are enormous, greatly dwarfing our own and those of almost all other creatures. The young are born from eggs, frequently unfertilized ones.

Under the microscope these are attractive little beings occurring in many colors and mottlings. They are important as fish food in larger ponds and they are doubtless scavengers themselves, helping to clarify the water. Their eggs, or maybe the adults, dormant within their little limy shells, lie safely through our long northern winters, like myriad seeds of plants, ready to become active from time to time when the spring sun warms the woodlands, the leaf pools, and the swamps and ponds where the ostracods and the daphnia also propagate in enormous numbers.

From a shady retreat in the wood lot float the perfect and varied phrases of a wood thrush. Over and over he offers them, and from various distances come the answers of rivals in this prolific population. Again there is that indescribable chainlike utterance created within that strange organ, the syrinx, in the throat of the veery, as songs are made in the throats of the other birds which inhabit our planet. Still other species now join in until the chorus is general, yet above all in volume, with a sharpness which is almost startling, sounds the master voice of a very special robin. Ever since this day I have thanked the inventor of the recorder especially, for the voice of this particular bird was truly enthralling. If you have ever taken the trouble to listen long and intently, you will have noticed, of course, how very greatly the songs of individual birds of a species may vary. In fact this is one of the most interesting and compelling facts of bird study. There are singers and singers among any group of birds, varying with their ages and their individualities just as there are among human beings. This robin possessed one of the richest and most powerful voices I have ever heard in a bird of this species. His tones rang over and through the woods, and *through me,* so filling me with pleasant sensations that at first I feared it must be an illusion of my enthusiasm. But no, much later, long after this nesting season had passed, when this artist's voice had dried up altogether until another year, when all of the summer birds had gone south once more, here was that whole wonderful spring chorus whenever I wanted to hear it, preserved for all time by the recorder in all of its richness, with this robin of robins chiming in at its climax. There is something strangely stirring in a dawn chorus played in one's bedroom in the dead of winter. It is so perfect that even the perfumes of the springtime woodland seem to envelop one.

There are other outstanding composers of avian song in other parts of the world which have deeply impressed me. Among the huge trees of the mature rain forest in British Guiana dwelt a cotinga called the bell bird,* whose startling notes were clear and enormously loud like the striking of a finely cast metal bell. Here also I heard the still more amazing "quadrill" wren,† living low down in the same forest, whose limber and versatile syrinx produced in rapid unpredictable sequences unbelievably sweet instrumentlike whistles which came in rapid succession from positions all over the scale— intensely high notes followed instantly by intensely low notes, or low notes jumping to high notes, then to lower or middle notes, or up or down again as suddenly, bringing to the listener one of the greatest experiences of tropical bird study. Would that I had owned my portable recorder in those days to catch those almost unbelievable voices.

In the equally great and beautiful subtropical forest of the Eastern Andes in Colombia, at a locality high above what was then the little village of Villavicencio, we were enchanted by the perfect antiphonic singing of pairs of big tawny-breasted wrens.‡ Here we obtained specimens for the American Museum of Natural History, and it was here, with the late Dr. Frank M. Chapman, then its Curator of Birds, and the late master bird artist Louis Agassiz Fuertes that I sat

* *Casmorhynchos niveus.*
† *Leucolepia musica musica.*
‡ *Thryothorus coraya caurensis.*

listening and experiencing for the first time this remarkable alternation of responses so perfectly timed between two wild creatures. It affected me deeply, and strange as it may seem I kept thinking of that old phrase, "two hearts that beat as one." These birds poured forth their antiphons, at first like the twanging of liquid wires, which changed then to gurgling sounds blending with those of a mountain brook by which we rested in the thick mossy hangings of this high humid forest.

Our seats were moss-covered boulders forty-five hundred feet above sea level. Here the forest was primeval, and Chapman loved this place which was one of the richest in birds which we had found, cool and delightful after the hard days which we had spent on the trails and in the heat far below at the comparatively more barren edge of the llanos (plains) which begin at the base of the Eastern Mountains. It was here in a single day, in a bag of sixty-six birds collected for the museum, we had thirty-four species, and in another single morning's work we obtained individuals belonging to thirty-eight different genera. Someday I hope to write more about Colombia in book form, the richest bird country of all.

The fact that birds sing as they do has never been explained. Of all the passerine species in the world probably not a great percentage of them sing either well or beautifully, but most all of them try to sing, that is the wonderful thing to keep in mind, for the birth of this emotion en masse, in creatures so far below man, constitutes a stumbling block for those who continue to argue that we live in naught but a mechanistic world of chance.

There are interesting puzzles here from an evolutionary standpoint also. In all of its main features for instance, the bird brain is like that of reptiles, yet, as far as I am aware, no reptile has ever evolved which could really sing or even approach such an accomplishment. In these cold-blooded

creatures, bound to the earth itself, or to the branches of trees
at best, there is not a spark of what we might call melodious
emotional song. A few reptiles, like the alligators, produce
vocal noises to be sure, but as musicians these creatures cannot even compete with frogs and toads, a group at which the
reptiles peer down their scaly noses with fine contempt from
their own somewhat higher niche in classification. And who
could conceive of either the amphibians or the reptiles, even
in a million years, evolving elaborate songs like the melodious
outpourings of grosbeak or bell bird, or the piping and
antiphonic wrens of the tropics? Birds and man—these are
the only real singers among all of the known creatures on
earth, and therein lies another mystery.

It is of course true that birds sing in a great many cases on
their chosen nesting territories for the purpose of advertis-
ing this fact to their specific rivals. It is true also that the
males dominate their mates through their vocal achievements. Likewise it is the accepted belief of most biologists
that birds are to a very great extent controlled by seasonal
behavior cycles, each act being "released" by a former act
automatically, notwithstanding the fact that I have observed
young sparrows barely out of the nest trying to copulate,
and have seen adult sparrow hawks many times apparently
succeeding in this act in winter. I do not believe that all of
their actions are automatically controlled, or that their songs
are always triggered by an invariable train of events. I believe
that like the robin whose voice I so enjoyed recording, like
the antiphonic wrens of Colombia which sing when it is not
necessarily their nesting season, like the starlings which sing
on sunny days all winter, they often do this because they like
to sing. In short, because they are at least capable to some
extent of experiencing emotional pleasure which springs
from their ability and their actual efforts to make and recognize these extraordinary sounds. Or must we obediently ac-

cept those dogmatic statements which claim that all of this melodic striving is purely automatic, instinctive, and the result of chance? Of course, as a matter of fact, neither I nor the avid behaviorists nor the scientists may say for sure, but at least in my own case I am happy in my own personal belief and viewpoint.

In concluding this chapter, let me quote the words of Charles Hartshorne who has made such penetrating studies of bird song.[1] "The most basic conclusion from evidence presented is perhaps this: birds, like ourselves, though in their own very limited fashion, are subject to the great principle of beauty, 'unity in variety.' Song may have developed from simple calls and/or random warbling to more complex and definite patterns whereby contrast is sharpened and made more effective; such patterns are then repeated, either with variations or at intervals long enough to allow the fading of vivid memory. Rarely indeed are patterns simply repeated over and over with scant pauses. This avoidance of mere repetition is what the principle of beauty demands, equally with the avoidance of mere change.

"Although such views seem anthropomorphic to some readers, will they not to others seem the logical way to include human reactions within the biological scheme?"

For my own part, the more I study birds at home and in the tropics, the more I am convinced that man and woman are not the only creatures producing songs for the pleasure of composing and listening to them.

CHAPTER 8

P.M. in the Wood Lot

THE keen observer and lover of nature has never far to travel to uncover intriguing situations, for these are commonplace in all the world of living things. My own curiosity became a lifelong habit which has sent me to hundreds of places. I believe, however, that it was mostly through my studies at home in familiar fields and wood lots that I first found inward harmony, satisfaction, and faith, which now I am trying to translate to my fellow men, not only through this and other books, but also through my work at the Bruce Museum. I know that there is nothing in nature which man may even begin to duplicate with his hands; nothing which he may describe adequately with a pen which equals firsthand observation and experience. The real thing is always far better and more inspiring in its intricate detail and beauty, but what is one to do with a consuming urge to share this wealth which is all about us, when so many human beings prefer to pass it by? Some of these experiences which are just beyond the boundaries of our daily routines, others somewhat more remote, I have tried to describe in these chapters, or I have endeavored to illustrate through the medium of paintings and dioramas within the museum, where each year thousands of adults and children may see them. I feel that even if only a few of my readers or visitors to the museum receive the intended messages of inspiration, all of the work and effort represented will have been doubly worth while.

The privacy of one's own wood lot is an ideal place for discovery, and no matter how small, such ownership is indeed something to be cherished. Of course it is true that in a tropical forest novelties and puzzles arise in greater and more bewildering profusion, and of many of these, more in later chapters, but if one must remain at home, compensation always comes in remembering that the backyard, the home garden and woodlands have never been completely explored, and that they harbor things worthy of long and careful consideration.

At the boundary of the lawn and wood lot grow a cluster of white oaks.* Having sprouted almost together, perhaps sixty or seventy years ago, they have grown up tall and slender for such trees, not broad-crowned like their fellows who live minus competition in the open. With their five- to nine-inch leaves, divided into lobes of varying sizes, they are useful in many ways. First, they supply pleasant shade for our outdoor grill. Their close-set group acts as a natural chimney up which all summer rise odorous hazes from charcoal fires over which steaks and lobsters broil, where bass and swordfish sizzle, and where kettles of littleneck clams send their heavenly salty aroma skyward.

Second, the higher branches of the oaks with their strangely involved twigs offer good nesting sites for woodland birds. Scarlet tanagers—all-too-brief visitors from Colombia and Peru—have twice raised their broods in one of them. Brilliant and colorful as any tropical creature, again I wonder what urges these birds northward on their annual migration, to sing and breed in your wood lot or mine, when the jungle

* *Quercus alba.*

forests seem so much more suitable as a year 'round environment.

Upon the undersides of the oak leaves in normal years
toward fall, crowds of plant lice ooze droplets of "honey-dew"
which doubtless makes them tasty bites for the smaller migrant birds. Again in spring, the same birds find the oak trees
prolific of "inch-worms," and sometimes in May, brilliant
blackburnian warblers, as many as six or eight together at
times, stand out orange and black against the foliage in the
sun's long rays of late afternoon. A small patch of woodland
is a truly wonderful thing, and at any season and at any
hour it yields to the investigator.

Astonishing furry balls as large as good-sized plums, containing many kernels and cells, grow rapidly upon white oak
twigs in spring. These are the work of tiny sawflies * belonging to the great insect order Hymenoptera. Some subtle
chemical injection transmitted through the ovipositor as the
insect places its eggs within the tissue of the plant, or perhaps a physical reaction caused by irritations of the minute,
feeding larvae, beget these pink, fur-covered combined incu-
bators and brooders which protect and feed the grubby offspring. No one knows how these abnormal growths called
galls are produced. There are hundreds of kinds in the United
States alone, and there is much to be discovered about this
subject. Perhaps the most interesting fact regarding galls is
that each species of gall insect or gall mite, however tiny,
creates a *diagnostic* edifice upon the plant in which its eggs
are deposited. There are homopterous galls made by aphids,
lepidopterous galls made by moths, dipterous galls made by
two-winged flies, and many other hymenopterous galls made
by sawflies and cynipids. Still others are made by mites,
which are eight-legged creatures and therefore not insects.

* *Callirhytis seminator.*

Most astonishing of all is the fact that all hymenopterous gall insects seem to be females. No one has ever seen a male.[1]

For years the author has been experimenting in an effort to produce galls artificially by the injection of gall and gall-maker extracts into leaves, so far unsuccessfully, but always with the hope of understanding more about this mystery. The material is all around us in many shapes and sizes. Many bear extraordinary decorations upon their exteriors, and there are truly amazing engineering problems which have been solved by nature within still other species such as the big round spotted oak galls, inside of which there are dozens of fine radii like threads supporting the central larval cell. All of these things are set up by the inexplicable blending of unknown substances formed within the plants, the insects, or mites, which will probably remain unknown to us. (Figure 17.)

In these days of considering ecological associations of major plants and animals in an environment as living wholes, we must also think of minute and microscopic associations in the same way. The protozoans of the weeds and grasses for instance, or those of the lichens, or those of the pond scums; or the collembolans and mites and other creatures of the bark world which we have come to know in other chapters of this book, and now these gall-makers and their specific plants. In ways far too cryptic for us to understand, it is possible that even they are bound together and perhaps mutually beneficial in certain cases. Of course this may not be so, but on the other hand who would have thought that the termites which help to reduce fallen stumps and logs to soil would be unable to digest their woody food without the aid of microscopic protozoans which live inside of the insects? Doubtless there are thousands of relationships and mysteries in these lesser worlds still to be discovered and understood. In the case of the termite and its internal helpers, the physical balance is so delicate that either perishes without the other.

All of these lesser associations must somehow in their turn fit into somewhat greater ones, and these into still greater ones, and so on until a chain is complete, which remains so until some rude influence, perhaps even the removal of a single plant or animal may upset the entire system which has been evolved.

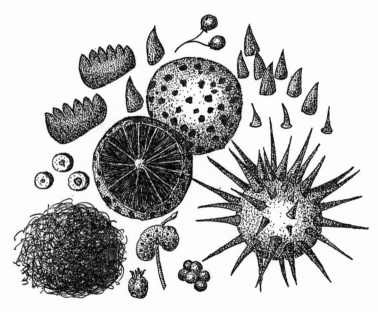

Figure 17. Common galls removed from leaves and twigs to show diagnostic forms (not drawn in relative proportion). Spotted oak galls in center, one cut open to show remarkable radii. Cock's-comb galls are from elm. The spiny ball forms on the wild rose, the kidney-shaped one on huckleberry. The cherrylike galls at top are produced on touch-me-not. Cone galls are abundant on witch hazel and hickory. The little cluster of "bullets" are from oak. The hairy gall is from rose, and the buttons from hackberry.

Complexity in the living is almost beyond belief, whether we are considering man or whale or protozoan; giant redwood, liverwort or desmid; whether a single organ or the smallest part thereof, and the naturalist or the researcher steeped in special problems often encounters almost hopeless cases, and then expresses his confusion and bafflement in the face of such findings in eloquent words.

To give a single example, there are tiny moths in my wood lot and yours which are known as the leaf-crumplers and leaf-skeletonizers, the leaf-work of whose little caterpillars most every country dweller has seen. In our storeroom there are others which feed on flour or oatmeal and similar foods, and which are usually mistaken for escapees from our unwatched clothes closets. These moths all belong to one of the numerous superfamilies known to entomologists as the Phycitinae, in which there are 619 named species and twenty-one subspecies. One scientist spent twenty-five years completing a 581-page quarto volume which describes these tiny creatures. For use in the same book, highly trained artists produced in minute detail, one thousand, one hundred and thirty-five greatly magnified illustrations of the *genital organs* of these moths. It is by examining these organs under the microscope that the hundreds of species are identified. It is the fact that these parts vary sufficiently in hundreds of cases to be diagnostic which is so astonishing and which I wish to emphasize. Here we discover the amazing sexual truth that for some unfathomable reason *it mattered* to nature that the genitals of this entire superfamily should differ.

Remember that this book by the late Carl Heinrich * on a single group of moths, one out of thousands of groups among hundreds of thousands of species of insects, convinced the author of his fundamental ignorance. Heinrich died in 1955

* Heinrich, Carl, *American Moths of the Superfamily Phycitinae*, Washington, D.C.: The Smithsonian Institution, 1956.

at the age of seventy-five after thirty-six years spent as an entomologist with the United States Department of Agriculture, but not before he had written: "When I began this study I had hoped to write a monographic treatise and explore the phylogeny (race history) of the family, but I now find that I know so much less than I thought I did and that the accumulated knowledge of others is so meager that any attempt along these lines would be a vain and futile performance. We do not know what a primitive phycitid was like. We do not know which forms evolved from which, or how. We weren't there. We may surmise; but the guess of one ignoramus is as good as that of another, and there is nothing to be gained by either."

All of these various differences, details found in little insects' parts, matter but little to human beings, but they *do* matter for some reason, otherwise all of these combinations of the genes which are responsible for each difference in the organs of each of the species would not have come to pass as we know they have. Year after year numbers of these tiny moths deposit their eggs upon leaves in my wood lot. Somewhere, also in my wood lot, there are many species of microscopic parasitic wasps, some of which are so small that their offspring are hatched *inside single eggs* of these moths. Here are represented thousands of other combinations of genes within the cells of these parasites, which control *their* genitals and the shapes and sizes of the ovipositors through which the microscopic eggs reach their destinations. Are there still more submicroscopic things living within the eggs of the parasites? Without a doubt, but I for one have not yet discovered them.

Moths which are attracted to the lights in our houses are often revelations in color and design if carefully examined, yet even these are usually dismissed as nuisances or dumped mentally at once into that all-inclusive category of "millers." Small wonder, then, that the vast multitude which I have spoken of as the Phycitinae have been studied by so few. I for one will henceforth look upon those little houses of the leaf-crumplers and the mining operations in chlorophyll of many of the others with wonder and delight. They hold fresh interest for me now, hiding, as we know they must, many secrets about life and sex and reproduction.

Each summer about the end of June or early in July moist spots appear around the edges of certain scars near the ground upon the butts of two of the white oaks already mentioned. How these scars came to be there I do not know for sure. They were there when our property was purchased some years before, but I have always suspected that they were the result of chafing where the new wood has endeavored to grow over partly embedded rock. The trees evidently grew up over and around these stones, and now on windy days there is just sufficient motion in the butts to continue the chafing and bring about the summer bleeding which has now become an annual affair. The scars are partly healed at their extreme edges where the new cambium and wood has tried to cover the rocks, but despite this, the trees ooze sap which soon becomes a sticky frothy mass as it first shows signs of fermentation.

About this time, minute grubs may be seen sluggishly wriggling within what to them is evidently a nourishing and delicious brew. At such a late date it does not seem possible that the sap would continue to ooze to the surface naturally as it does in early spring. I believe that this seepage is due in part at least to the irritations set up by these creatures, either through the exudation of a solvent, or because they are actually chewing and feeding upon the tissue of the trees. To be truthful, however, I do not know. Whatever the cause, as the annual phenomenon continues, minute yellow bubbles appear in hundreds. These soon multiply into thousands and hundreds of thousands which at a little distance appear as a slightly yellowish froth. As myriad new bubbles form, older ones burst their envelopes, and as these legions continue to explode, minute gassy messages are released into the wood lot which collectively cause the odor and the irresistible lure which brings a number of additional sylvan organisms hotfoot to this fermenting mass.

First to arrive at these free saloons are the vigorous white-faced hornets,* those violently stinging black-and-white-bodied ones, which, through the efforts of successive summer broods, evolve from the original one inch, queen-built globe, those huge top-shaped castles of excellent and variegated gray paper. All hornets seem to love sap, and how they delight in this particular boozy brew! In the fall also, when the yellow-bellied sapsucker pecks rows of drinking holes in the weeping willows, the late hornet broods and many other insects flock to this oddly scented fluid, where some get drunk and are eaten by migrant birds.

A few days after the native hornets commence to feed at the oak bars, another, larger, introduced species, whose ocher-and-brown body may measure over an inch in length, appears upon the scene.† As in the other species of hornets, colonies of these big wasps arise in a single season from queens which have hibernated. Their large, elongate nests are constructed of a brittle paper, laid on in wavy bands of ocher and brown, gray and cream-color, quite different from the globe- or top-shaped structures of indigenous species.

These two kinds of hornets, as well as many other kinds of insects, seem to pay little or no attention to one another when sap-feeding. They come and go, and share the free liquor in harmony, but late in June more belligerent actors

* *Vespa maculata.*
† *Vespa crabro,* a colonial species introduced from Europe, now common here.

arrive upon the scene. Surprisingly enough these are butter-flies; the red admiral which is found upon the wing from May until late in September, and that species of briefer life-span, the modest pearly-eye, seen only from late June until the end of July.* The former are robust creatures spreading nearly two and one half inches, and real beauties when fresh from the chrysalis—forewings of smoky velvet with bands of orange-red and much white spotting, underwings with orange bands along their margins. The pearly-eyes are more delicately fashioned and colored and somewhat smaller than their rivals. Their forewings are pale yellowish-brown, with darker yellow-bordered eye-spots, while their undersides are still lighter, marked with wavy bands of bluish-white and brown, the eye-spots here touched with white in their centers.

The latter seem always to be found in little groups or popu-lations, locally isolated, like the little annual gathering at the oak trees in our wood lot. Despite their delicate make-up they are domineering creatures. Almost as soon as they have left their chrysalids and have expanded and dried their wings, they appear at the bubbling saloons, commencing at once to vie with each other for food and for the opposite sex as each female happens along. They are quick and per-sistent where the sap is juiciest, but so are the red admirals at these preferred positions. The two species now about balance each other in dominance and physical roughness. They flip their wings, advance upon each other, threaten and pursue, yet neither seems able to drive the other perma-nently from the rich saporiums.

Now, a great deal has been written in regard to the so-called brilliant "warning colors" of insects and other forms of life, but as often as not, in the opinion of the author, such highly colored spots and bands and patterns have been mis-

* *Vanessa atalanta,* the red admiral, and *Lethe portlandia,* the pearly-eye.

takenly linked and interpreted. The red admirals are a case in point, and while their flashing red bands are distinctly arresting to the human eye, they fail to frighten either the pearly-eyes or the hornets, who merely move to one side, when with extra bravado an admiral comes near or even occasionally touches one of them with its flipping wings.

A short distance beyond the oak bars, however, a well-stocked grain tray caters to crowds of red-winged blackbirds, the rival males by swelling their gorgeous shoulder patches easily intimidating new arrivals, and thus proving in this analogous situation that the "warning color" theory sometimes holds.

Again there was the case of the crested flycatchers which nested in a box placed in one of the oak trees within thirty feet of the drinkers congregated at the annual debauch. Watching constantly as the young flycatchers were being fed, it was surprising to learn that a large part of their diet, especially during their final days in the nest, consisted of butterflies. Not fragments or de-winged bodies, but *whole ones* of many kinds were taken directly into the nest box, which was so constructed that I could pull a tin slide and look within the instant the old birds departed. Even big butterflies, such as the familiar tiger swallowtail with a wing-spread of nearly four inches, were presented to the youngsters whole, and not so much as a small fragment of either wings or body could be found in the nest directly afterward. That the flycatchers were consuming such supposedly distasteful items entire was positively established, but this is not all. Over and over again, and oftener than any other butterfly species, the parent birds were bringing red admirals. These flycatchers were launched upon a veritable orgy of butterfly destruction. If the red bands on the butterflies' wings are supposed to act as "hands off" signals to predators, these flycatcher observations surely negated the theory once more, for here was a definite and serious one all but exterminating the local red admiral population during that season.

In our wood lot live at least eleven species of beautiful moths known to entomologists as the "underwings" or *Catocala* moths. Their underwings are gorgeously colored in some species with wide bands of orange or yellow or exquisite pink, contrasting sharply with bands and spots of black. Conspicuous as these smaller wings are, their larger forewings are among the most perfectly camouflaged objects in nature, blending perfectly with the colors and streakings of bark. Immediately upon alighting on a chosen surface, the forewings are folded over the smaller ones and the moth's body in the form of a gable roof. Observing them thus in natural woodland settings, usually on the undersides of limbs, we realize that only animals with the keenest visual perception could detect them. Let one be disturbed by day, however, and off it darts erratically through the woods, and now according to the warning-color theory, its brilliant bands crying loudly, "Hands off, I am not fit to eat." But from our simple observations it is plain that in their two pairs of wings these moths are contradictory. One set indicates safety and edibility, the other colored pair, the opposite, so here once again the theory does not make sense.

The subject of edible or distasteful insects brings us inevitably to that threadbare case of the "bad tasting" monarch butterfly, and its "mimic" the viceroy, insects belonging to different genera, and both of which occasionally drift through our wood lot toward the Buddleia bushes beyond.* The monarch is the big tawny, white-spotted butterfly known to most everyone, and in the north, except in size, the viceroy does resemble the monarch closely. It has been supposed by many that the latter gains immunity from its "enemies" by

---

* *Danaus plexippus* and *Limenitis archippus.*

being mistaken for the monarch, a story which has been repeated so frequently that no one ever seems to question it.

But it so happens that we have long raised Rhesus and African green monkeys at the Bruce Museum, animals which are the food-testing tools supreme.* Both of these species ate monarch butterflies which were offered to them. They also accepted red admirals and several other kinds. Discarding the wings, they consumed the bodies bit by bit, as though enjoying a novel flavor and experience. Monkeys cannot be fooled, and they will immediately detect the tiniest portion of any bitter drug no matter how well it has been hidden in their food, spitting it out disdainfully and without a moment's hesitation. In the case of the monarch and the viceroy, I believe that they fit into the category of parallel evolution very well indeed, an explanation, however, which will doubtless be cast aside by critics in their preference for the older and perhaps more dramatic one.

There are organisms within our wood lot which may be plants or which may be animals. They live chiefly in a decaying woodpile and they are known as the slime molds, or Myxomycetes. There are several kinds of these cryptic things, but one group in particular is indeed an enigma. Minute amoeboid independent cells which are animal-like develop from spores which are of course plantlike. These cells increase in number by division, but do not fuse into a multinucleate mass. Animal-like they now feed upon bacteria, but when their food supply becomes reduced or dried out, thousands of the amoeboid cells start to move, all by some wonderful sense, toward a common center, where they next unite in a mass or great gathering, but each cell retains its individuality. This army of cells, over-all perhaps but a millimeter

* *Macaca* (*Rhesus*) *mulatta* and *Cercopithecus aethiops sabaeus.*

or so in length, now sets forth, a creeping, living co-ordinated whole, the individual cells gliding or rolling over each other and traveling considerable distances along the rotting log on which this amazing thing was born from a spore. This mass of protoplasm seems to have definite polarity—a sort of head end and tail end, and if the head part of the mass is scraped off and carefully grafted into another part of the whole, it will there organize matters as a mass of "head" cells with a following of its own, made up of the remaining mass, which forthwith follows the grafted "leaders" in an entirely new direction. Finally, the whole mass or pseudo-plasmodium, as it is called, stops moving and sends up a stalk which the mass eventually overruns and is then converted into the spore body from which new slime molds are born again. The entire phenomenon is a mystery of the first order, and no one can explain how these amoeba-like objects change into a variety of cell types at different periods of the organism's life history, starting as we have seen as typical plant spores.

Turning over the damp leaves of the woodland carpet, earthworms pull back their strange elastic bodies, pink or brown, with iridescence playing about their scores of segments. A few yards away in the garden soil a strange breed of greenish earthworms is abundant. If they are importations they are harmless foreigners, and like our native *Lumbricus* they help aerate the soil with their burrows, and in passing it through their gizzards and body factories to obtain its nourishment, they pay their way by enriching the remainder and depositing it in little sculptured lumps upon the surface once more. All who have read Darwin are familiar with these particular annelid activities, but what these common creatures now bring to mind once more is that recurring enigma of regeneration, for the earthworm, if pulled in two by fisherman or beast or robin, without much ado or trouble regenerates the portion which escapes, and then goes right on living and growing again. In the same environment with the earthworms dwell delicate orange-brown salamanders, creatures with vermilion-dotted skins as smooth and beautiful as though just freshly created or painted. They hide under leaves or logs, and sometimes after gentle night rains they prowl the woodland in hundreds until after dawn. This is the land phase of the newt, one of our common salamanders, which later returns to live out its life in the pond where it was born. No one knows why it repairs to the land for a considerable portion of its life, nor why its colors are then so brilliant and so radically different from those which it later wears in the final aquatic form.

These creatures are endowed with the powers of regeneration to a remarkable degree. I once found one which had had both of its forelimbs bitten off, one of them well above the elbow, yet it was not found in a faint or a state of coma like the one before referred to, although its injuries seemed serious and very recent. Taking the little creature into my laboratory and carefully coaxing it to enjoy a diet of white termites, to my delight and astonishment both of its limbs soon commenced to grow again. I would not have been quite so surprised had only the longest injured limb exhibited this wonderful power, but to witness even the more deeply offended member slowly but surely directing its miraculous cells to multiply, and to build themselves, like intricately fashioned blocks of a temple, first only into a blunt outgrowth, but gradually to evolve a whole new elbow, a new forearm, and finally beautiful tiny new fingers, complete with normal bones and nerves and a circulatory system as well, and all within the course of a few weeks, remains as one of the most beautiful and impressive revelations I have experienced.

Here is something which we actually know very little about. In the case of the newt it is believed that the process is dependent upon the nerves remaining within the injured parts, and also to the return of certain cells to their embryonic abilities. Whatever has been found out in regard to such cases of regeneration, the fact remains that we do not know what *induces* the cells to perform such miracles in a salamander, whereas regeneration of a limb by the cells which produce a man remains impossible.

Not long ago as an experiment in regeneration, I placed a single short log freshly cut from a large willow tree in an upright position, with the end of this section of the tree which had formerly been uppermost now reversed and standing on very wet ground. In six weeks this reversed section had sent many long white roots into the ground, and nearly fifty small new branches with normal leaves skyward. One "wrong" end had developed the roots, and its other "wrong" end had created limbs and foliage. The battle against extinction had been so strong and so valiantly waged that a whole new little tree had come into being almost before the wood of the old one had had time to dry out. The great riddle here lies in the ability of the willow's cells, apparently *anywhere in its being,* to form roots or branches or intricate leaf factories in the right place at the right time. Comparatively we might say that it is as if we human beings might grow feet when standing upon our headless necks, or a head from the stump of either footless leg.

Regeneration is of course based upon cell multiplication, and we know through the delicate experiments performed by the biologist Hämmerling [2] that the nucleus of the cell is necessary to the sum of the processes concerned in building protoplasm, or in other words, underlying growth itself. Now there exists a very interesting marine alga called *Acetabu-*

laria, and while this is but a single-celled organism, it is extraordinarily large, measuring up to nearly two inches in length. It is a delicate, more or less calcified * species of green alga native to the waters of the warmer seas. Possibly it takes its name from the Roman *acetabulum,* a little cup or saucerlike object which was used for vinegar. Actually the alga resembles a little toadstool in form. In any case the important point as far as the experiments were concerned lay in the fact that this plant, despite its size, possessed but a single nucleus.

When the biologist cut off the toadstool-like cap and most of the attached stalk, leaving the nucleus in the smaller part of the stem and its base, this nucleated fragment not only lived, but it regenerated the umbrella-shaped cap completely and then continued to go on living normally. The larger remaining part of the alga with its original cap, now deprived of a nucleus, soon withered and died, its drive to live extinguished and the organism unable to regenerate the missing parts of its body.

We learn from the two plant examples just described that the cells in the wood or bark of the willow, minute as they may be, but present in enormous numbers, represent a much more efficient regenerative system than that which exists in the *Acetabularia.* In the willow we have such crowds of cells that even if they are destroyed in great numbers as they were in cutting the whole original tree into logs, there are still enough nucleated ones to beget new roots and branches and foliage wherever the plant may need them. The alga, on the other hand, may only regenerate itself if its single nucleus remains uninjured.

While we seem to see here at once the superiority of the

* Made stony by the deposition of lime in its make-up.

multicelled organism through these plant observations, we wonder anew at the restriction or absence of regeneration in the higher creatures including man. Here is one of the great puzzles of biology, and up against such unanswered questions as this we see indeed that our ignorance is a sea.

No living naturalist or scientist can explain the ability of the living plant cell to change itself internally, to change its chemistry perhaps, and its whole normal differential direction as conditions dictate. Here the mandate to live is carried out with a vengeance, successful, imponderable, faith-building.

The seasons come and go and always they bring new and interesting events in the wood lot, but there is one which never varies in its significance.

It is now late in the wood lot and it is fall. Contemplating the leaves as they drift downward, objects which directly or indirectly have been the sustaining food of so many creatures, I find them symbolic of the organic life-span itself. In every falling leaf there is a reminder which is my story, your story, and the story of all living things, but here condensed as in a time-lapse motion picture. The eager bud, swelling and impatient to expand, is our childhood; the darkening, roughening, and coarsening of the summer epidermis is the fading of the bloom of youth, and in the slowly drying tissues and the dying of color, we see what at first we dismiss optimistically within ourselves—those inevitable signals that a return to the earth is our eventual lot also, and that it is but a matter of a little more time than that allotted to the leaves. In actual time-lapse motion pictures which I have made of blossoms, the stages are recapitulated even more graphically, for here upon the screen we see in seconds the unfolding of the bud, the perfection of the fully opened flower, and then the slow writhing and withering stepped up in speed, which leads to life's earthly exit. This is the story of the wood lot and its creatures and its vegetation, and the story of human beings as well. No one knows what follows, but faith gives us hope that the descent to earth is temporary; that this may be but the preparation for our future.

CHAPTER 9

Sound Water and a Mooring Chain

IT WAS one of those days in late summer when the visibility
was almost unbelievable, a day which might well have been
the despair of an artist in search of "atmosphere," but one
which was a joy to the lover of sunlight. To the east of where
we lay in our old thirty-two-foot cruiser, Smith's Reef stood
out black but barnacled at low tide. Long Neck Point lay
off our port bow, and although we were far inshore, the
lighthouse on Eaton's Neck, Long Island, several miles across
the Sound stood out clear and magnified above the ocher
cliffs with their green thatch of trees. It seemed but a short
swim away on this brilliant day, and to the eastward we
could follow the dim ribbon of land toward the great arc
of Smithtown Bay as it faded into the purple water far on
the way to Greenport.

With engine idling and gentle wavelets lapping our sides,
I lazed with my companion contentedly aft, dabbling hand
lines and spreaders, hook baited with fresh-caught spearing,
for, as most fishermen would guess, the "snappers" were in.
Daily they were rushing to the inlets on the rising tides,
there to feast upon these sweet-fleshed shiners. Born in the
inlets in early summer, spearing are always sweet and tasty
fish food. The "snapper" run is heralded by the arrival of the
baby fish close to shore when the tiny spearing are also there

in legions. For weeks both species seem to grow in proper ratio, forming two nicely regulated links in a food chain wherein the larger fish find the smaller ones adjusted to their growth, until having crossed that mysterious invisible line, "snappers" suddenly become bluefish and forthwith depart in search of bigger game in the deeper waters of the Sound or the ocean. Early each summer the baby blues arrive in numbers, yet no one seems to know what bluefish eggs are like or where they are deposited. Common as the adults are, I know of no one who has ever found a bluefish roe. Have you?

Over occasional grog we yarned and delved into the nature of things. All at once my companion's good eye commenced to dilate. "Spearing on the rising tide," he exclaimed, "millions of them. Boy, those snappers know what's good! How about a pot of deep fat; fish dumped in while kicking; eat 'em, heads, eyes, guts, and all?" The idea sounded good to me. After all, *whitebait,* you know, is simply mass baby spearing fried whole.

We watched cautiously for the next upsurge of the school, our big umbrella net stretched and ready, then suddenly to our amazement we were gazing not upon the sea-green and silver bannerlike bodies of closely packed spearing, but into the midst of an enormous mass of alewives and sea herring. How cautious and how beautifully alert they were. At our slightest movement the entire army of thousands would turn, answering as one that marvelous, inexplicable signal which somehow surges instantly into the collective brains of such massed pelagic creatures. No matter how spread out they might now become, no matter how densely they might be packed the next instant; even when parted into two compact, darkly flowing streams around some bit of kelp or weed, all would shift to the left or to the right, or about face, or dive in a flash to safer depths as one, at some mysterious command.

Keeping very still, we now saw them come to the surface, where in a body they commenced to nibble at something quite invisible from where we watched. So numerous was this school that these thousands of mouths blew a frothy curtain upon the surface composed of myriad tiny bubbles. Again and again the school alternately dove and rose, fed and dove once more. Except where the school was browsing, the water of the Sound looked as it almost always does on a calm day in summer. Certainly to the casual bather or the captain upon the bridge or deck of his boat or yacht it would have seemed just like any other Sound water under a brilliant sun on a cloudless day. Not so to this great crowd of herring, however, fish which we had never before seen here at this season, and which were finding something very much to their liking, food particles in quantity evidently, so here was something well worth investigating.

From the collecting outfit we brought forth a special type of net, a ten-inch bronze ring from which hung a cone of the finest bolting cloth. At the small end of the two foot bag, a small opening was fitted with tapes sewn to the netting. Three bronze wires led from the ring to a swivel and towing line, and a strainer of heavier mesh material covered the mouth of the trap. Before tossing this overboard, the hole at the small end was closed by means of the tapes, and long vials of sea water were made ready for our catches.

Next, the heavy duty engine was run very slowly with the propeller in gear as we described wide circles, towing the net fifty feet behind, with everything so adjusted that it remained only slightly below the surface. Thus for a time we swept the territory of the now-departed herring before allowing the boat to drift with engine idling once more while we hauled in the apparatus.

It should be explained here that bolting cloth comes in 0, 6, 12, and 20 gauges. Gauge 0 has 38 meshes to the inch, gauge 20 has 173. You will realize therefore what an exclusive sieve a net made from this finest material offered.

Upon examination, we now found a jellylike mass at the small end of the cone. It was perhaps an inch in depth, greenish in color, and translucent. At first glance this could easily have been mistaken for a single small jellyfish or ctenophore, but actually it was far more interesting than that, as we quickly found out when the tapes were loosened and the mass gently worked into the receiving vial of sea water.

A remarkable thing now happened, the mass of "jelly" melting away and spreading out like pale rolling vapor, thus rapidly clouding the formerly clear water in the bottle. In this blob of stuff which we shall call "tow," we had thousands of those tiny entities which swarm upon or near the surface of almost all waters at times, the basic foodstuff of the oceans upon which so many millions of other creatures depend for their existence. We call this living manna *plankton* —the minute, wandering, passively floating, or weakly swimming plants and animals, their spores and eggs and larvae which inhabit the waters in countless millions. In this particular mass the plants were mostly diatoms and blue-green algae—the Cyanophyceae—while the minute animals were protozoans and entomostracans, including the all-important organic fish food known as copepods which are found in dozens of curious-looking species. In addition to these we had the grotesque early stages of crabs and barnacles which look nothing like their parents; scarcely recognizable young starfish and sea worms, the developing embryos of fish in their floating egg castles, and dozens of the minutest of jellyfish.

Plankton is so rich in life forms that it often changes the color of water. In billions these organisms are born, in billions they die day after day. Their dead are the sea's fertilizers, the living the sea's restaurant and pantry. Plankton stand pre-eminent in the economy of the lakes and the seas and the oceans. (Figure 18.) How many bathers realize as they swim and gulp in and expel the water as they progress that they may be taking in and throwing out thousands of floating or kicking, but completely harmless, organisms? How many yachtsmen are aware of the billions of these microscopic things through which their boats plough on every trip or cruise? Look closely at the water on some calm summer day when the sun is shining brightly and no wind stirs the surface. The liquid is everywhere flecked with minute specks of light reflected from the cells or bodies of living things, reminding one of the lighted dust moats floating through a sunbeam in the air. This is the plankton which you see and no human being can estimate their numbers.

Under the binocular microscope a drop of "tow" reveals a new and startling world again. The uninitiate would find it hard to believe his eyes, much less would he connect many of these fantastic creatures with their much larger and familiar adult forms. Youthful crabs, known as zoea, are goblins in miniature yet amazingly beautiful beneath the powerful lenses, with their long beaks, bristles and horns, and their gorgeous eyes. Spinoid sea-worm larvae look like animated, bristle-covered seeds even in a single drop of fluid, while young starfish in what is known as the pluteus stage resemble the cocks used in the badminton game. Among the algae and diatoms, the strange peridiniums, and the other microscopic plants, there are additional bewildering forms, highly colored at times within their casings and pellicles and decorations of glassy threads or luminous beads.

The plankton plant forms sustain themselves upon the natural inorganic foods dissolved within the waters, and upon the nourishing disintegration products of other organic remains. Upon the diatoms, those very important crustaceans called copepods feed. It has been estimated that ten thousand

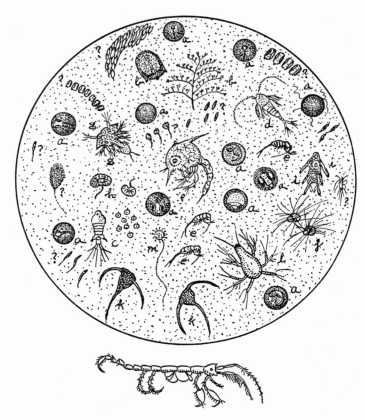

Figure 18. Approximate appearance of plankton organisms. Not drawn in relative sizes, all greatly enlarged. (a) Hatching fish eggs, one with attached parasites; (b) two stages of a polyp, one plantlike; (c, d, e) copepods; (f) zoea stage of a crab; (g) nauplius stage of a barnacle; (h) Nocticula; (i) pluteus stage of a barnacle; (j) larval stage of a spinoid sea worm; (k) a dinoflagellate (*Ceratum*); (l) larval form of a shrimp; (m) *Podophrya,* a creature found riding a caprellid. Other forms in circle are unidentified. Outside the circle, *below:* A female caprellid, somewhat enlarged.

pounds of these minute marine plants would be required to build one thousand pounds of copepod bodies. Stomach and intestinal examinations of some of the herring which we caught here soon revealed that they were indeed feeding to a considerable extent upon these copepods. Again it has been estimated that one thousand pounds of copepods would be necessary to insure one hundred pounds of herring. To carry the food-chain facts still further, one hundred pounds of herring would build ten pounds of mackerel, the swift species which preys upon them, yet it would take one hundred pounds of mackerel to build a pound or two of a human being. Biologists have made these estimates. I do not know how.

The paragraph above relates but a single one among hundreds of cases which might be cited to illustrate ecological relationships in the waters, in this case illustrating even a relationship between man and the microscopic organisms of Long Island Sound and the Atlantic Ocean. When we stop to think of the millions of pounds of fish which the human race consumes annually, and then compare the figures above with the almost unimaginable numbers of tiny organisms which are alone necessary in order that baby fish of thousands of species may get a nourishing start in life, and then become the food of larger ones, we marvel. When we contemplate the intricate chemistry which has been necessarily evolved in the sea and which has brought about the proper conditions of balance so that all kinds of life may be properly fed at all stages, and that each species may survive and propagate, we can but wonder again in reverence and humility.

Let us go back now to the original plankton haul on that pleasant day. Everyone who dwells along the salt-water shores has had encounters with barnacles, those curious crustaceans in their sharp-edged abodes. Our own boat had hundreds of them adhering to its bottom, and yachtsmen scrape them off angrily, twice yearly in warm waters, while bathers get scratched regularly by their ever-present shells upon rocks and piles. Most of us ignore them unless they injure us, but the barnacle animal itself is a wonderful little creature. With every rising tide their feathery arms protrude from thousands of neatly opening and closing shutters to wave their shares of the plankton mouthwards. In the vial of "tow" we had dozens of barnacles in baby form, gentle limpidities possessed of six active appendages. These newborn ones called nauplii are at first free to roam where they will, but after a short time a strange urge comes over them and commands them to cease their wanderings. They settle down upon what to them seem suitable places, where they attach themselves and soon construct those beautifully protective houses fitted with valves or shutters which open and close as precisely and perfectly as any which might be designed and made by man with the aid of his most ingenious machinery. Of all the crustaceans in the world, I believe the barnacles are the only ones born free which give up their freedom at a certain time to attach themselves for life to other objects. At first thought this would seem to be rather a stupid regression, but is it? By fastening themselves to ships these delicate little creatures have long obtained transportation, house and all, to all of the interesting and exciting ports of the world. Possibly some of them even take around-the-world cruises, free, on the bottoms of the finest ocean liners.

The vial of "tow" yielded eggs of several sizes which were visible to the naked eye, and which had been ejected by unidentified carefree parents. From their perilous journeys they had been rescued by chance, and these were soon transferred to little dishes of sea water. Small as their inmates were, I felt more akin to them than to the rest of the plankton, when through the microscope I recognized them as embryonic

fishes and saw their minute hearts already pumping streams
of corpuscles which rolled along through transparent arteries
and veins and capillaries, millions of minute disks flowing
through systems of tubular brooklets. These were vertebrates
developing just as we do, with backbones, blood, and familiar
organs. Invisible within these eggs at the outset had been
minerals also, snatched originally from the sea, but now as
we have seen in some way transformed into the supporting
bones of fishes, however tiny in their present state. Despite
the millions upon millions of eggs which are spawned so
carelessly into the sea, I marveled that even these few which
had been rescued by our plankton net had escaped the perils
of their medium long enough to enter it.

On summer nights the Sound is sometimes alive with a
flagellate protozoan called *Noctiluca*. Comparatively large
beside many of the other plankton organisms, they appear
when greatly magnified rather beanlike in shape with somewhat twisted "tails." Simple as these creatures look, they are
extremely complex organisms, somehow endowed with the
property of luminescence as well, a gift whose inner secrets
no one has been able to explain. *Noctiluca* swarming in billions is often the "phosphorescence" of the sounds and seas
and oceans, known at times to every seasoned swimmer and
to every nautical traveler, whether by rowboat or ocean liner.
On a memorable night on Long Island Sound we once found
them in such fabulous numbers that the slightest agitation of
the water—the plunging of an oar, or the tossing of the
smallest object into their world—brought the instant greenish glow of heatless light from myriad microscopic globes,
beautiful beyond description. As we dove from the deck of
our drifting cruiser into the glassy Sound late at night and
swam naked among them, our bodies seemed to be igniting
thousands of tiny sparks, and when we swam far down agitating them, we left glowing trails as though we might be mis-

placed comets fallen into the sea. How could plankton, the baby fish, the snappers, and all of the other larger animals of the Sound go hungry in such a pantry as we were exploring?

Plankton is seasonal to a great extent. Winter months in this region represent the arctic night for these organisms of the Sound, yet silica and other minerals leached out of the land and carried to the saline waters by rivers and streams are accumulating throughout the cold months as well as at other times. In March, April, and May there is a great awakening, for now compounds of nitrogen and phosphorus, and many other nourishing minerals and salts, and organic substances from the disintegration of once living things have surged to the surface water layers from the cold bottom. Once again, under the stimulus of the longer sunny days, life cycles swing into higher and higher gear also, until the waters swarm with plant and animal forms. While this is true of the Sound, we have the apparent anomaly that such life is more prolific in the colder ocean currents than in warmer waters. There is no comparison for instance, in numbers of organisms found in the warm blue water of the Caribbean and the cold Humboldt Current of the West Coast of South America, the much colder waters far outstripping the warmer in richness of living things, a fact which has always been a puzzle to me.

When we raised our mooring late in the fall we found that its iron chain had become a museum, or I should say, a zoo of pelagic life. Crowds of dark-blue mussels and a few yellow-rayed ones had grown upon it like so many badly parked automobiles. Every available space seemed at first to have been occupied by adults, but closer examination revealed that hundreds of tiny ones were crammed in among their elders, and that all were fastened to the chain or to each other's shells by bunches of black threads or byssuses which are secreted in the foot of the mussels. There were hundreds of barnacles also, settled here for life upon these shells, whence they had come as nauplii earlier in the year. In the maze of mussels, sea worms lived and fed, and squat little crabs had also taken up quarters here where a rich association assured a constant and varied food supply. It eliminated for the little mobile inhabitants the necessity of more dangerous safari out into open waters, for edible things literally swarmed upon the shells of both the mussels and crabs, upon waving strands of attached seaweed, and in the slimy algae growing upon the living whole. Here upon this mooring chain alone was sufficient material about which to write an interesting book, a worthy project for someone in the future.

Of all the living creatures of this assemblage, suddenly discovered skeleton shrimps (Caprellidae) were the most intriguing, and no one, it would seem, has had very much to say in popular language in regard to these odd little amphipod crustaceans. Books which I have read were not very helpful. Even Rachel Carson in her delightful work *The Edge of the Sea* says nothing about their lives, nor do they appear in her index, although she figures them in a drawing, but Dr. Minor in his 888-page volume on seashore life [1] does tell how to identify several well-known species, which are illustrated very clearly.

Caprellids are seemingly aberrations of the shrimp clan, deviators or wanderers from the normal which somebody has called "nobody" crabs. Studying them closely, it gradually dawns upon the observer that in their make-up there are parts and segments of their bodies and appendages which in turn suggest parts of lobsters and crabs, conventional shrimps, and still other kinds of crustaceans, but all of which seem to have strayed a bit from the usual. In the species which inhabited the mooring chain,* the head shell was spiked in front, the thorax was short, and the long slender remainder of the body was composed of numerous oddly formed segments. Beginning at the head, there were two pairs of bristled antennae, followed by two pairs of gnathopods ending in swollen portions and suggesting in purpose a lobster's pinching claws. From the third and fourth segments of the body, padlike gills protruded, while two pairs of segmented legs ending in convenient grasping hooks were attached to segments four and five. These odd shrimps were almost white and somewhat less than an inch in length, and the females were identified by sacs filled with eggs which they carried beneath their shells. These creatures are among the most curious arthropods, and indeed there are no other living things just like them. (See Figure 18, p. 137.)

Examining the mooring chain on this particular day was like a voyage of discovery. Up until this time I had never found such creatures as skeleton shrimps but as often happens after finding something for the first time, the feat seems to be easily duplicated thereafter, and I have come across them several times since while searching marine growth from the Sound. Doubtless they had been present always, but in my ignorance I had passed them by.

At first sight both my companion and I had mistaken the clustering white objects for networks of bryozoans, or bits of dead and well-bleached vegetation, but suddenly the "dead" objects commenced to loop their bodies after the manner of "inchworm" caterpillars. What we had found seemed to constitute a whole convention of caprellids, or perhaps a gathering of a very special nature for some unknown reason, for there were at least a hundred individuals in one closely packed group alone. I rushed them home to a tank of sea water and marine algae lest they die of exposure

* *Caprella geometrica.*

in the air, and here the masses slowly separated, each shrimp taking up an individual position upon the plant life. Once situated to their satisfaction, they would cling fast with their leg-hooks and then stand straight out from their supports like so many pole acrobats at the climax of the act. This was their feeding method. In their natural habitat they reached out thus into the water of every incoming tide, gnathopods in readiness, and on the alert for any bit of food or flotsam which the waters might waft in their direction, and looking for all the world like bits of marine vegetation.

I believe that copepods, those tinier, diatom-feeding crustaceans of the Sound in summer and fall, are the natural food of the caprellids, but once I observed one holding a bit of sea grass and perhaps gleaning from it what under the microscope proved to be herds of protozoans which existed in thousands upon the vegetation. My skeleton shrimp in this case seemed to be lapping this living broth, as we in forgetting our manners might enjoy some delicious sea-flavored chowder. *Maybe* this was the case. I do not know for sure what this caprellid was eating.

Now it is a very interesting fact that the thin, baglike objects which hang down from the third and fourth segments of caprellids occasionally have protozoans living upon them also. These bags, I believe, are the gills of the shrimps, and these other organisms are probably there simply by chance. One of these gill sacs measured only three millimeters in length and had no appreciable thickness. Nevertheless, there was sufficient room upon it for numerous protozoans of a most remarkable sort. Under the most powerful lenses of my binocular microscope these creatures looked like tiny globes stuck full of pins whose heads were wreathed with suctorial tentacles, and each of these bristling balls was tethered at the end of a very fine thread or stalk. These were undoubtedly *preying creatures* in ultra miniature; riding in a colony upon the single gill sac of a caprellid, and thus traveling wherever the shrimp might go. With their wreathes of tentacles these organisms were doubtless capturing still more minute, and maybe even unknown organisms, and these in turn were devouring still smaller things, and so on, down the ladder of life, for no one knows how many additional rungs are in this wonderful tapestry of the sea. I can only write with inadequate words of what I saw with bewilderment through the microscope, but I was delighted to find that other biologists had already found this all but invisible protozoan pincushion and had named it *Podophrya gracilis.* (See Figure 18, page 137.)

I have no idea what newborn caprellids look like, nor where their eggs are deposited, or what may be the other details of their life history, but some day I hope to find these things out personally. Meanwhile, in the presence of so many billions of marine organisms which we know exist, we cannot help but wonder what magic is locked within the water itself. Let us therefore make a casual examination in the laboratory.

Filtering off a random quantity to remove the dirt and foreign matter, we find with an accurate measuring-beaker that we have exactly one hundred and twenty-four cubic centimeters of the fluid left. Removing this filtrate to a porcelain evaporating dish and placing it over a copper water bath or steamer, we heat it thus over boiling water until all of the sea water has evaporated. Now very carefully recovering the resulting residue and weighing it, we find that even in this small water volume there were ten full grams of solids. In these glistening white compounds or salts which were obtained so easily by these elementary laboratory methods, lies the whole astonishing yet simple secret, for whether it be water from Long Island Sound or water from the middle of the ocean, these great fluid bodies are indeed rich mineral mines.

Were we to make a more careful examination and separate the major life elements from the compounds in our sample, we would find such things as potassium, sodium, calcium, magnesium, sulphur, and carbon, without which life would be impossible. What we loosely refer to as "salt water" also contains those halogens known as chlorine, bromine, and iodine. There is also copper and gold and many other elements which may or may not be so important to living things.

You have of course tasted sea water, and in the course of natural events you have doubtless also tasted your blood. Think back now for a minute and you will realize that these two fluids taste very much the same. Actual analysis has shown that both of them contain many substances in common, some of the elements listed above in somewhat similar proportions. Feeling quite certain that life originated in the sea, and that land animals evolved from aquatic ancestors, we realize that the pioneer creatures which first ventured ashore must have carried the sea with them, either in simple, bathed interiors, or in primitive circulatory systems, and that blood was eventually evolved from its essences. Now, except for changes in it due to the elapsed ages since that emergence, we human beings at the top of the evolutionary ladder still carry these essences in our veins and arteries. To this very day the fluids in our bodies link us forever as blood brothers to the sea.

Perhaps that is why the sea still calls to us so strongly. Perhaps that is why man so willingly still goes down to the sea in ships.

CHAPTER 10

Four Tropical Forests

Part I.   Dominica

$\mathbf{A}$T SOMETIME during the life of most everyone, I believe there comes a yearning for the wilderness. In the
hearts of naturalists this longing is incessant; in the hearts
of others it may be intermittent or even only there unconsciously, but it is there nevertheless, and when it comes to
the surface it is strong.

It is spawned in many a bed—in the near vacuum of dull
routine; in the offending sounds and the abrading confusions
of towns and cities; in the endless puerilities to which we
are subjected over the air waves; in self-resentment at one's
toleration without revolt, but most of all it is spawned in an
innate homing instinct, somewhat atrophied though it may
be, for the odors and sensations, and the experiences of freedom which long ago favored man in his less complicated
and less artificial environments. Breathing noisome gases,
amid dust and dirt and the stenches of industry, amid smog
and the poisons emanating from incineration and the fall-out
from too much experimentation, is it any wonder that our
anatomies cry out for help, for untarnished sunlight, for the
pulmotor of pure air which is to be found in all its original
goodness only in the filtered isles of the wilderness?

This yearning to be somewhere else is indeed very American. Graphically it is illustrated by the annual exodus, that great vacation outpouring, that fanning out of the people each summer, like the irresistible outwash from high mountains to a plain before the force of a cloudburst. I believe that this movement is an inborn, partly unconscious response to a latent sense within us. Some are content to go only a little way, others have the urge to find oases, but civilized ones further from home; but for a lucky minority who possess the wherewithal, and who are neither discouraged by the effort which must be put forth, nor the discomforts which may be encountered, the tonic and emotional impact of life in the wilderness may be the reward.

This chapter has been divided into four parts because of its length. It concerns aspects of the complex wildlife in four tropical environments, all of which were forested ones. My difficulty has been to know what to eliminate among the hundreds of interesting things which were encountered, but by combining experiences in the four into one chapter, perhaps another purpose will be fulfilled—to bring the feeling of the tropical forests home to the reader more graphically, with all their luring charms and unsolved mysteries.

"Grand were the mountains—rising fantastically in turrets, spires and precipices, wooded to their very tops. Innumerable waterfalls plunged over the cliffs and hung like suspended threads of silver. . . . Seen for the first time by European eyes, this coast is like nothing else in our workaday world; a landscape rather of some fantastic dream."

So wrote Nordhoff and Hall, or one of them, enchanted by memories of an island paradise in *Mutiny on the Bounty.* This happy paragraph and the quotations from Robert Louis Stevenson and Pierre Loti on pages 179 and 171 were penned about fair islands of the Pacific, which, alas, most of us will never be so fortunate as to see for ourselves; but, reader, take heart, for any one of these famous descriptions might well have been written about island and mainland mountains and jungles which lie but a few days away by steamship, and only hours away by plane, from that colder and duller and more familiar island called Manhattan.

Come with me now on four of these journeys, one to the high mountains and forests of Dominica in the West Indies, one to the big jungle which lies along the Mazaruni and Cuyuni rivers in British Guiana, one to a bit of superb rain forest filling a deep pocket high between the shoulders of the Colombian Andes, and a fourth to that forested island of Barro Colorado in Panama, where one lives in comfort, with untouched wildlife at one's door. In these places I spent supreme days of adventure as a naturalist surrounded by new sights and sounds, odors and revelations.

Less than two thousand miles from New York in the Lesser Antilles lies that island in the sun affectionately called "Honeysuckle Dom'in·eeka" by the colored natives, spelled Dominica in the books; mountainous, precipitous, so thickly forested and so deluged by rain in its Caribbean and Atlantic setting that it is at once the equal in beauty of anything which the South Seas may have to offer.

I believe that from a naturalist's standpoint I am as intimately familiar with this island's forest and mountain conditions as anyone living, having tramped, ridden, and camped, photographed and searched there from sea level to cloud forest, and to the weird bromeliad-covered summits of what are the West Indies' highest mountains. As far as I know, no one has reached these summits and reported on them since I did some years ago.[1]

For many days the great forest at eighteen hundred feet around our leaky shack had been swept by those torrential rains and whirling winds known only in such places. At first they filled one with awe and startled surprise, especially during those blackest of nights when there was no moon behind the storm clouds to slightly lighten the sky. As water slammed against shutters, closed over glassless windows, and dozens of hungry bats squeaked their high-pitched chiropterous protests from behind rotting boards and hand-hewn shingles, you realized that of your own free will here you were at last, after years of desire, in the heart of these mountains where over three hundred inches of rain descends in a single year, in a shack without lights or heat or plumbing, or even a good roof to keep the water out. Until the prayed-for sun should burn away the leaden clouds and suddenly reveal the deep-green mountains, gold-washed and steaming in all their splendor, you might feel for a time that this whole thing had indeed been a great mistake. But the impact of this sun-bathed scenery, its odors, and its strange voices both night and day, reassured one completely after every storm.

Because of all this rain in the Dominican mountains the roar of tumbling waters is characteristic of its subtropical zones. Cloudbursts move rocks and boulders to the valleys with frightening determination, and at times erosion is too plainly evident for comfort, as when my companion and I came close to being "eroded" ourselves. A flash flood had rushed down from far above us and almost caught us as we clambered up a safety tree which we had cut to reach the bottom of a deep rain-carrier, and wherein a minute later we watched large rocks rolling along like pills, and saw them hurtled out of this chute into space at its outlet upon a sheer cliff face, like pellets from a bean-blower, and then heard them crash with sharp echoing violence upon other rocks in the valley far below. The wall of water had come down with the speed of a *nuée ardente* from an erupting volcano. Had we not had a tree with purposely cut climbable limb stubs with which to get out, our bones, like those rocks, would doubtless be down in that valley somewhere yet.

The first creature to baffle me in Dominica was a nocturnal one whose ringing musical notes the natives said was the "blacksmith beetle beating his anvil." After searching with the aid of my flashlight for nights on end without success because of the uncanny ventriloquial properties of these sounds, the thing suddenly "went off" within inches of my ear as I was washing photographic negatives in buckets of brook water within the pitchblack improvised darkroom under the shack. It startled me so that I nearly upset the precious buckets. Covering the negatives with a focusing cloth, I grabbed the flashlight and quickly found my "blacksmith," a huge, quivering, leaf-brown tree cricket, waving its enormously long antennae and holding its sound-producing wing-covers almost perpendicularly over its body as it clung to a post supporting the floor above.

Normally these insects filled niches here and there in the big forest with their unique sounds, notes which one might imagine could easily be caused by a hammer striking an especially tuned silver anvil several times in succession, thus the native name was appropriate enough, although the creature involved was a cricket instead of a beetle. The sound was altogether delightful at a distance, but when inches away from one's ears, the powerful vibrations were so loud and penetrating as to be truly startling.

Forest sounds in great contrast were the harsh, unmusical, and at times almost deafening scrapings which issued from the wing devices of huge locusts, whose fat bodies were superbly camouflaged in deep green, light brown, and sepia, like the splendid matching bark upon which they often rested, with their huge leaping legs, armored with many sharp spikes, drawn up and ready for instant action. They called insolently from high and sometimes hollow tree trunks which then amplified the din tremendously, and again from the very sides of our shack. "Crack-crack—crack-crack—crack-crack," they repeated over and over again for hours at a stretch, sending out these primitive insistent directives to the opposite sex, and magnifying their suggestive summons by means of devices especially evolved in the construction of their chitinous wing-covers.*

Examining these devices very carefully, in both the tree crickets and the big locusts, I found them differing widely in detail, but not in their basic sound-producing idea. Both worked on the "pick-and-tooth" principle. On one wing-cover there was a series of ridges or tines over which an especially shaped and stiffened edge of the opposite cover was moved, somewhat as a pick moves across the strings of a musical instrument. When the insects were sound-producing in life, both wing-covers were held up perpendicularly or nearly so, and the movement of the picking implement across the tines varied in speed, according to the species, and probably according to the temperature. An idea of how the process works in its simplest form may be gained by scraping a fingernail across the top of a fine-tooth comb. In the case of these crickets and locusts, however, sounds were produced by what we might term living instruments. In the giant tree crickets,† which made sounds like striking tuned metal, the microscope revealed two hundred and eighty ridges in its wing device, shaped like little decked-over boats or dories placed side by side, with a sharp ridge running from end to end along the top center of each. There were also very fine points or spines for some unknown purpose, situated at each end of each of these ridges or tines, and the entire series

---

* Chitin is the horny substance forming the outer integument or skeleton of insects.
† *Paragryllus martini.*

diminished in size toward the right side of the wing-cover along a gently bowed wing vein. Remember that these tines, as I have called them for convenience, were too small to see clearly with the naked eye. The microscope also revealed a tear-shaped well, apparently for arresting sound vibrations, close to the scraping portion or "pick" on the opposite wing-cover. This whole apparatus was seen to be delicately fashioned and put together with the greatest of care, almost as if it had been purposely designed for a creature destined to become a musician.

Much simpler, and much more coarsely constructed sound devices had evolved in the case of the three-and-one-half-inch, fat-bodied locusts.* The microscope showed at once why the notes of these insects were so different and so much less pleasing than those of the lighter-bodied tree cricket. The ridges or tines, for instance, numbered but twenty-five. They were heavily built, bluntly rounded upon their upper surfaces, and diminished rapidly in size along a short, sharply down-turned, heavy vein, while the stiff picking device upon the other wing-cover was placed at the inner edge of a squarish drumlike enclosure which was doubtless an amplifier. My approximate drawings in Figure 19, showing the two devices together, will doubtless clarify my descriptions.

Remember that a vibrating body may transmit this movement to another body having a larger surface, which in turn, amplifies the sound by setting a greater amount of air in motion. If, for instance, the tines of a fork are twanged so that they ring, and then the fork handle is pressed upon a table or some other hard surface, the sound vibrations are immediately amplified. Likewise, when the tines of an insect's sound apparatus are scraped by the edge of the other wing-cover, similar amplification seems to result, for here the tines and the pick as well press upon the extensive and intri-

* *Nesophyllidium fulvicosta.*

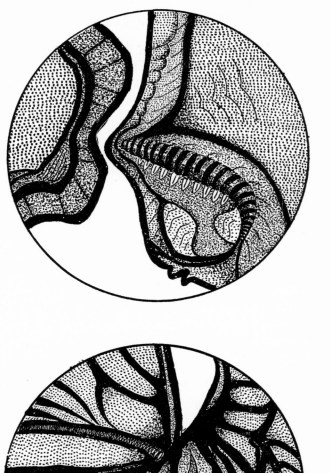

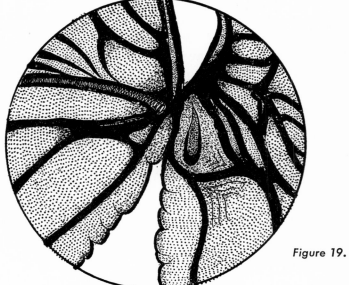

Figure 19.

cately formed remainders of these wing-covers. Whether or not, in the cricket's case, the source gives off pure tones consisting of single waves, or "fundamental waves plus harmonics," my ear was of course not sensitive enough to discern, but to me the notes of this insect seemed pure and musical at a distance, whereas those of the locusts were monotonous noises.

In physics we learned that a *musical* tone is heard only if the vibrations caused at its source have a definite frequency. On the other hand, if these vibrations are irregularly timed, or roughly ground out like a saw ripping wood, we have what we human beings call a noise. In view of these facts it was no surprise to find the two very differently built sound-producing devices in these two insects after hearing them.

What we have observed about these sound devices brings up many questions. Why, we must ask, should the tree cricket be endowed with musical ability, whereas the big locust, belonging to the same order, may only emit harsh noises irritating to the human ear? And why are the notes of the former so amazingly ventriloquial? Unlike the human ventriloquist, who creates the illusion by suggestion that his altered voice issues from the dummy, or from some other location, our tree cricket accomplishes the same end unconsciously in the black of night. I defy anyone to find the source of these anvil-like notes within the forest except by chance, for the sound always comes from where the searcher is not, and we have a ventriloquist operating by some different and apparently unexplained principle. Suffice to say that no one on the island of Dominica had been able to find and

---

Figure 19. Top: The twenty-five-tine, coarse sound device of a *Nesophyllidium* locust of Dominica. Bottom: The 280-tine, much more delicate sound device of a *Paragryllus* tree cricket of Dominica. Both magnified several times.

definitely identify the insect as the maker of the "blacksmith" sounds until I did by great good luck. We wonder also how natural selection might account for these intricate sound devices, how such things could have *begun to evolve*, and why among insects they should have evolved at all, and then over and over again in the order Orthoptera, but only in a comparatively few other kinds of insects such as the cicadas.* This fiddling of only certain insects, isolated with their "music" as it were, in a huge sea of "uncultured" silent orders, families, genera, and species, is something which no one can explain.

In the walls of the shack we heard ghostly tappings at night, now here, now there, now overhead. When we found the creatures this time, we could scarcely believe our eyes, for no others could have been more grotesque than these pale-gray gecko lizards.† They hid behind the boards by day, appearing at dusk to feed upon insects which were attracted by our newly acquired kerosene lamps. They crawled about upside down with the greatest of ease by means of dislike divisions of their toes. They not only astonished us, but they amused us with their weird set expressions.

Colonies of bats were always with us. Some of them fed their babies periodically during clear nights. Others seemed to stay away until morning, while the majority fed from dusk until dark and then holed up again, bellies filled with well-chewed insects. All in concert produced a peeved or jocund din, according to their changing moods—irritations caused by the rude shoving and jostling of arrivals hunting for their accustomed positions, or the contenting comfort of other

* The order Orthoptera includes the long-horned grasshoppers and katydids, the crickets, the locusts, and a number of others. The cicadas which are also noted for their loud strident "songs" belong to a different order.

† *Thecodactylus rapicaudus.*

warm snuggling bodies. Bats, as we know, are predominantly feeders upon winged insects, yet strange to say, no flying mammals evolved before them to take advantage of this enormous food supply, and bats not until millions of years after insects became abundant. Remember, too, that bats are the only mammals among thousands of kinds which ever evolved their own wings, something which is indeed a mystery.

On one side of the shack under the loose shingles lived the *Molossus major* clique, some fifty dusky-furred individuals with tails as distinct as those of shrews. On the north side we had the *Tadarida antillularum* clan, a very dark, homely-faced lot whose tails were even longer, while still other larger species swooped about in the gloom in the trails at dusk, and I found tiny ones which lived in thousands in the nauseating breath of a deep volcanic fissure high in the mountains.*

From the dense blackness, especially on the wettest nights, came the pleasing sounds from the throats of little tree frogs. The wetter it was the more they piped, and by the light of a hurricane lantern I watched their impassioned choruses issuing from low and glistening leafen platforms. The frogs were delicate little things with gold-rimmed eyes, their bodies of various shades of ocher and brown, and some with camouflaging lighter stripes resembling the mid-ribs of dead leaves traversing the center of their backs. All had that delighted wide-awake expression which only wet and courting frogs can have. From their cream-colored throats, balloons out of all proportion would suddenly expand like blobs of bubble gum, and as these little wind machines rose and fell, there came the sweet-toned penetrating sounds. "Co-leet—co-leet," they seemed to say, with enormous persistence from dark

---

* The larger ones in the trails were yellowish-brown leaf-nosed bats, *Monophyllus luciae*. The little cave bats, six of which I could easily put in the palm of my hand, were the species *Myotis dominicensis*.

until late at night, and the females must have been charmed indeed by such dulcet and energetic harmony.

Among so many individuals I thought it would be a simple thing to work out the life history of this creature, and perhaps add something to their lore besides their burdensome technical name,* but the frogs occupied a habitat, let us not forget, of enormous rainfall, and this very condition, as it turned out, made the project more difficult than it had appeared. From the Caribbean Sea and the Atlantic Ocean, both of which lap Dominica's shores, the tropical sun sucks up great quantities of water, then the cold-topped mountains draw it back again as torrential rain, dumped from the dense clouds which almost always hang over them. There are rivers and streams and brooklets on every side as a consequence—one for each day in the year it is said—which, it would seem, should offer ideal breeding conditions, but diligent searching in these waters yielded not a single one of the frogs' polliwogs, nor their eggs.

Days of searching continued to slip by; a month, two months, without success, and now I began to believe that it was not the breeding season. Then one day I sat down on a log in the wet forest to think this thing out, when all at once it dawned upon me. The waters all around me were not still enough, that was it. The rivers were at once too large and too swift for singly deposited eggs, and they would be washed away at once and soon out to sea. The smaller streams were mostly rain carriers leading from the higher mountains. They might contain some small safe pools one day which might be violently churning on the next. Of still, permanent pools there appeared to be none at all, for in Dominica in the forested mountains the land everywhere consisted of steep sidehills as our aching muscles often reminded us. Even puddles and ditches near habitations were useless to the frogs when they

---

* *Eleutherodactylus martinicensis.*

formed, for they were inhabited by predaceous insect larvae which preyed upon all smaller living things. The damp wells of the bromeliads, those epiphytic, pointed-leaved plants which grow so commonly on tropical trees might have afforded good breeding places except for the presence of unique and ravenous brown birds called trembleurs,* which dug into these bromeliad grab-bags with their long, down-curved bills. They ate most anything, including occasional luckless adult tree frogs, and tadpoles would have been succulent delicacies.

More anxious days passed. The end of the trip was in sight. Then at last I found the eggs. Under a tangle of vines and shaded deeply by huge trees, I saw the crystal-clear spheres upon the forest floor itself, and with the discovery came what to me was a story both new and of absorbing interest, a story whose like typifies the lure which sends naturalists into all the odd places for the mere satisfaction of experiencing them. Nothing has ever brought me greater joy or deeper satisfaction than finding these little prizes. The precious eggs lay sparkling on the forest mold, and when I say sparkling I am not exaggerating, for a little star seemed to be shining upon the exterior of every jelly globe. No gems were ever gathered with greater care.

At the moment of discovery, I could not of course be absolutely certain that these were the eggs of *Eleutherodactylus*. They were not in a mass, but strung out in little lines of three or four, and then again they had been dropped singly. They might have been mistaken for eggs of some big tropical slug, but a few days after removing them to the shack for study, I observed with excitement that the cream-colored embryos developing within the spheres were assuming definite lines, not those of conventional tadpoles, but those of minute well-formed frogs. With a hand lens I could

* *Cinclocerthia ruficauda.*

see that the little beings bore vestiges of a one-time useful tadpole tail, an observation suggesting thousands of years of evolutionary change since the ancestor of this frog at this stage of its life was a free-swimming creature like the young of so many other amphibian species. Evolution had been at work here in earnest, and had succeeded flawlessly in adapting this one to the extraordinary conditions of its environment. Long before the truth became evident, the comparatively huge size of the eggs, compared to that of the adult frog's one-inch body, or compared to the much smaller eggs of much larger frogs and toads at home, indicated that something quite out of the ordinary in life history was to be disclosed, and here were frogs which skipped the free tadpole stage altogether it afterwards turned out.

How could this have come to pass? Of course we do not know, but it is fun to speculate. Probably this species reached the island from the mainland ages before. Maybe ages before that, it deposited its eggs in water like most other common frogs. Let us remember that in the case of our familiar northern green frogs and hop-toads, the embryo moves to the outside of the jelly egg as development advances, there to remain for a while before taking up its active swimming existence. Now, if a tadpole were to find itself emerging into damp air near the forest floor instead of actually into water, its normal reaction would be to wriggle back into the more hospitable jelly once more. Such an event could have represented the birth of a new habit. Thus, perhaps, may early *Eleutherodactylus* have initiated a move for survival, which through endless repetition, and increasing periods spent within the egg waiting for suitable exterior conditions, finally became a fixed part of the life history, eventually solving the problem of development completely within eggs deposited out of water.

Through the crystal walls of these eggs we may trace the

ancestral stages in some detail, a marvelous experience as seen through the binocular microscope. Watching the whole rapid development of the tiny frog, from a single cell to a perfect miniature of its already diminutive parent, was an experience which produced something in me akin to what Einstein called "a rapturous amazement at the harmony of natural law," and evidence of "an intelligence of such superiority that, compared with it, all the systematic thinking and acting of human beings is an utterly insignificant reflection." We must not forget either, that in these tiny entities which are all around us, much of the same creative ability is present which we find ourselves. Those little crystal eggs of *Eleutherodactylus* for instance, lying upon the moist forest floor, each knew a spermatozoon, depended upon one, and had to await its arrival before continuing upon its destined job, just as the human ovum must await the entry of a microscopic triggering entity to insure the creation of a human child. It is a wonderful truth, not a degrading one, to realize such kinships. It is a still more wonderful and inexplicable thing that we human beings are capable of consciously visualizing such events and of communicating them to others.

At first as I watched with the microscope there was little to see within an egg save the pale yolk within the three-eighths inch sphere. Soon, however, there were two cells floating where there had been only the parent cell before. Then, as segmentation got under way in earnest, these two became four, the four eight, and so on and on, doubling as we know they do, until I lost track of the endless numbers of cells which were aligning themselves in the usual miraculous manner into separate organs, tissues, and nascent bones, and after many days, into the tiniest of recognizable limbs, a head, and a tail, and into all of which gradually came the power of visible motion.

Still some time before ermergence, the little creature began to exercise its tail energetically at the slightest vibration from without, graphically signaling to my eyes a reaction which bore a message from this frog's long past history when once it passed through a free tadpole stage. At length pigment commenced to color the former translucent tissues. It appeared in stellate figures of black. Gradually expanding out of these pigment stars, long arms charted their courses through the tissues like flights of barely moving rockets, then joining ever so gradually, they filled the lighter spaces between. Next, the tail was slowly absorbed, and the great day at length arrived. All moist with birth, out stepped the Lilliputian perfectly formed frog, the smallest perfect frog imaginable. Peering from wide orbs of black and gold, it surveyed for the first time its niche in the great forest world, a mere speck of life, successful in an environment in which a human being might easily perish without special equipment.

Behold then, an amphibian which has reached, at least in many points of its life history, a position equal with the land reptiles, for the young *Eleutherodactylus* skips the free-swimming stage of most frogs and toads altogether. Selection must have played an important part in what has happened here, and it is easy to visualize the slightly larger jelly spheres and the slightly larger yolk masses evolving together and being selected, as being responsible through the centuries for the surviving individuals. Once on their own, the little frogs fed upon collembolans and mites and soft-bodied grubs and many other insects, but the inevitable food ring turned here as everywhere else in nature, and they were devoured themselves by a slim black-and-white snake whose only name is *Leiamadophis juliae*.

During the second field trip to this intriguing mountainous island, my companion and I struggled to the summits of its two highest and most curious "peaks." Of greatest importance was the camping trip to the top of Mount Diablotin, which is pronounced Di'·ablo·teen, for the purpose of obtaining first-hand knowledge and impressions, for no one who had ever gone up there had reported accurately on the plant and animal life.

While Diablotin is not a very high mountain—only 4550 feet as recorded by our own aneroids—when I state that we struggled to the top, I mean just that, for conditions on this climb are in some places possibly unique. We will skip all of the ascent, from the gorgeous climax forest which grows up to the 2500 foot level, to the real difficulties above, which arise in parts of the elfin woodland or cloud forest proper—a mass of tangled, stunted trees, distorted by winds, and draped with great tangles of vines, epiphytes, and deep mats of saturated mosses. These trees were literally staggering under their clinging blackened loads, and the whole area was saturated with slime and water which soaked and blackened the traveler. Under foot there was slippery mud and clay, and as the ascent grew steeper and steeper and the vegetation more tangled, progress was exhausting. As a final obstacle, we came upon a wide area of these gnarled and moss encased trees which grew *straight out* from the mountain and from slopes so steep that further progress could only be made by climbing hand over hand, or crawling like sloths through their slippery branches for what seemed like interminable distances. The camp packs and the guns, and especially the 5 x 7 camera outfit and *glass* plates which I carried at that time, seemed heavier with every move. This mountain has turned back many a would-be climber through the years.*

Those curious plants called bromeliads, which grew so thickly among the trees on the ascent, descended to the

* See *The Mountains of Dominica* by the author. Natural History Magazine, Vol. XXIX, No. 6, Nov.-Dec., 1929, pp. 585-610.

ground as the more open summit was reached, and here they
all but carpeted the ground, a fantastic sight with whole
strings of them sometimes stemmed together and their structure plainly indicating their pineapple family relationship.
Wherever there was space available between them, the
ground was aglow with lichens of many shades, and brilliant
emerald mosses. There were even occasional large fungi of
the edible morel group also, and low bushes profuse with
orange-colored blossoms penetrated the bromeliad legions.
Here and there a single kaklin or figi tree stood out, a species
whose thick, rounded, padlike leaves exuded a black gum
when bruised and which never washed out of our clothes
thereafter. Even a few small coarse palms rose like ghosts
through the scudding masses of cold clouds which almost
continually swept the summit, while scattered masses of
black rock peaking through this otherwise solid vegetable
world were the only reminders that this was an ancient volcanic mountain on an island which in other localities yielded
a lake of boiling mud, hissing blow holes, and steaming hot
water streams which poured from cracks into cold river water
below.

There was animal life up on Diablotin also—hummingbirds;
big olive- and brown-spotted thrushes which ate land snails,
cracking them and leaving little piles of shells around stone
anvils; parrots; the ubiquitous little frogs, and other land
molluscs or snails found only in Dominica.*

Previous to our climb I had directed our six black porters
and cutlass-wielders to build an *adjoupa* 3400 feet up on one
of the only partly level shoulders that we had encountered.
An *adjoupa* is a sapling-framed lean-to thatched with palm
fronds. These men set one up with vicious energy, *if they like
you*, in a matter of hours, a beautiful, skillful job, dry and

---

* *Amphicyclotus amethystinus.*

strong, with a projecting fly overhanging the open front. Your floor, however, is just plain mud.

A certain night which we spent in this *adjoupa* was of particular interest to me. An enormous fire blazed in front of us as we lay on our cots, a fire started with soaking branches and chopped-up saplings by means of great lumps of gum from the gommier trees, which had been gathered all along the lower parts of the mountain. This is a hydrocarbon which burns violently, once ignited. It oozes from slashes, dozens of them made by natives as they encounter these trees, thus there are running wounds building up the gum always ready for every mountain traveler. To the blazing saplings, logs and larger logs, then whole tree trunks were added.

There is nothing like a huge green-wood fire. It dried our saturated clothes in short order, while good rum warmed our innards. With the help of my companion, Dickinson S. Cummings, we cooked wild yams, aptly named "yarm savarge" in the native patois, and two big tins of erbswurst soup, one for ourselves and one for the men, who had built themselves a less elaborate *adjoupa* near by. Shivering in the unaccustomed cold, they had raised themselves two feet above the mud upon a bed of saplings bound to the frame of the hut with lianas. Some of them threatened to leave us at this point, but with our hot thick soup and a share of the rum in their bellies, they soon cheered up enormously. They bantered and argued and laughed, and in patois dubbed my companion "tombe-tombe-tombe" amid uproarious laughter because he had fallen down again and again, cursing mountains in general on the upward journey. For warmth in the night the men lay in a compact row like so many sardines, heads toward the fire. Soon after supper, exhausted from the climbing and falling and carrying, we all went quickly to sleep.

Hours later I was awakened by a terrific downpour which extinguished both of the fires. I could hear nothing at first but the roar of the solid rain sheet falling upon the forest and the *adjoupa,* like the roar of a train crossing a high iron bridge. It was a marvel to me that the others slept through it, but perhaps the rum had something to do with it. I lay staring into the utter blackness, and thinking how strange and wonderful it was that here I was at last, after years of planning this expedition, actually resting in the forest well over halfway to the summit of the highest of these mountains past which I had sailed on four former occasions, always gazing at their alluring cloud-embraced masses with my binoculars, and dreaming of that day when I would know first-hand what it was like up there. Now I was seeing it for myself, photographing it, and refuting some of the ridiculous stories and statements which had been handed out to me down at Roseau and at the other coastal towns by people who had never been up here.

A curious odor sifted in from the blackness as a shift in the wind dispelled the smell of wet ashes. The odor was sweetish, a body emanation, no doubt from an animal. Odors stimulate the imagination. What animal might it be? Why did it have this peculiar scent? Why did it possess such a special scent in the first place? How little our present-day senses tell us definitely when in the wilderness. I was a human being, but now I knew less than a mouse would under similar circumstances. I did realize, however, that this would have been a desirable odor to a man in need of food, for it meant that game was in this forest, agoutis or some other species of rodent perhaps. Then I also remembered that in British Guiana, these common mammals resembling overgrown guinea pigs did not seem to send out smells perceptible to a human being at all. In that mainland environment there were too many enemies which would follow such a pleasant, odorous, and obvious invitation right through to a rapid kill.

Maybe this odor came from a slow-moving mountain dweller like the 'possum. That a species lived in Dominica,* I knew, and when I once found a native smoking one's body over a slow fire high on another part of these mountains, its exact likeness to those which get into my garbage cans in Connecticut startled me, and reminded me graphically of the evolutionary puzzle with which this ancient mammal confronts us. My thoughts now wandered backward as I lay in the *adjoupa*. I thought of the Cretaceous period, about a hundred million years before. Even then it is supposed, the 'possum existed much like it is today, this living relic or what? Way back in the Cretaceous period it apparently reached the end of its evolution, but no one has ever found out why. In any event, the 'possum represents a wonderful case of viability, and despite its slowness and its sluggish brain, much less in volume than that of many much smaller mammals, it held its own, right up to the present day, not only in the wilderness, but amid all the hazards of an expanding civilization.

Up on Diablotin, a very safe place, I imagined an animal could smell any way it pleased without incurring any particular dangers, but then again maybe I was on the wrong track altogether. Who in the world actually knew what creatures lived up on this ancient mountain? Indeed there were terrifying things according to some of the island's imaginative inhabitants. Maybe this strange odor was the way pterodactyles smelled. Like the very ancient mammal, the 'possum, maybe there was one still alive on Mt. Diablotin. After all, you know, until 1938 it was supposed that the deep-sea coelacanth had been extinct for millions of years, perhaps even longer than the flying reptiles.

Such were my musings and my wishful thinking, but I never did find out any more about the source of the odor which so stimulated it in the darkness, and then the rain

* *Didelphis marsupialis.*

had let up, and all about the *adjoupa* the tree frogs commenced to call again, and were answered by others and still others, a collective chorus which indicated that these *Eleutherodactylus* frogs constituted a continuous, one-species population, despite their numerous color variations and patterns, which reached from far down below our base camp at 1400 feet, to the topmost moss of Diablotin where I found one.

And now came the strangest occurrence of this particular night in the *adjoupa* camp, something rather mysterious, but a repetition of an experience which we had passed through three years before at a much lower altitude. Being still awake I was lying in my cot chewing a delicious white stick of cabbage-palm heart collected on the upward journey. Suddenly the breeze shifted, then stopped abruptly, and strangely enough all of the frogs stopped calling. After a little while, a sound came which was like the faint roar of distant surf, but the Atlantic shore, which we later found out was visible from the mountain summit, was too far away for this to be the source. All at once the foliage stirred and then seemed to tremble, and as I threw a flashlight beam upward, the shaggy black moss upon some of the outlined trees sparkled with captured rain drops. Now the sound grew rapidly louder and louder, then, suddenly, my blankets and those of my companion, and even the cots themselves seemed to be fighting against a powerful sucking force, and in another instant all were awakened by a violent twisting wind which roared about the two *adjoupas,* bending them and tearing away palm fronds which went whirling out into the night. Before we could decide what to do next, the thing had departed again with a diminishing roar exactly like that of its approach in reverse. It did us no real harm other than to frighten us momentarily, but it left us wondering what strange combinations of wind and currents, temperatures and mountain contour gave birth to these baby tornadoes, for such they were.

When dawn came and I lay in my cot gazing comfortably to the westward, I could see through huge rents in the branches of tall trees whose butts were anchored in the soil of a slope far below our level, rents which had now been increased since the original enormous wounds suffered in the hurricane of a year before. Thirty-four hundred feet below, jutting far out into the bluish morning haze which rose from a dull sapphire Caribbean, two green and yellow hills, connected to the rest of the steeply rising island by a narrow neck of land, raised their smooth forms above a perfect crescent bay. As the sun came up, the eastern flanks of the mountains and the facing sides of the tree trunks were bathed in gold and white, and now my eyes and thoughts became concentrated upon those countless epiphytic bromeliads thriving upon the tree branches, and upon hundreds of the lesser kaklin trees below.* These trees with their thick, padlike leaves are characteristic of the strange elfin forests of the high wet regions of Dominica. Still another species of *Clusia,* a smaller one, grew up in taller trees and let down its roots to the forest floor for sustenance. The bromeliads seemed to grow upon all kinds of trees, but not as parasites, obtaining their moisture from clouds and rain, and their food from organic material accumulated within the leaf bases. These strange plants belong to the family Bromeliaceae, which includes some *nine hundred* species, and to which the edible pineapple belongs.

The tough, sometimes troughlike leaves of the hundreds of specimens in sight from the *adjoupa,* were arranged in more

* *Clusia venosa.*

or less regular whorls around large central buds. These leaves caught water which formed pools of dark sediment-filled liquid in their depths, a natural broth steeped in complicated nourishing substances and ideal as a medium for minute living creatures. In these depths, bits of wind-blown moss and lichen, fragments of twiglets and dead insects, and who knows what, rotted and particled and blended into a fluid soup of a wondrous nature. Here were hundreds of tiny laboratories and factories and culture jars, all working perfectly without human supervision in the bases of epiphytes, up in the branches of trees, upon an old volcanic mountain, on an isolated island in the ocean.

When we returned from the summit, after writing copious notes and impressions, and after obtaining the first photographs ever taken of the summit vegetation, and the first views from the highest point, which were shot through occasional holes in the clouds which surrounded us, I collected vials of fluid and sediment from the leaf pools of nearly one hundred bromeliads, and carried it carefully with the rest of our outfit, back down to the base camp at fourteen hundred feet, on the edge of the little gorge above the Du Blanc River.

Here, at leisure, under the fly of our comfortable tent, I made a thorough examination of the bromeliad fluids with the binocular microscope. From fluid brought from the very top of Diablotin, I recovered small earthworms. Living here also were the larvae of midges and other flies, but of greatest interest to me were the myriads of microscopic creatures living in solutions taken at various altitudes. Here again were those nameless billions, which, for lack of a better name and sufficient knowledge, throughout this book I have called the gyrating dots. Barely visible with the most powerful lenses I had with me, they were nevertheless present in such fabulous numbers in some of the vials of fluid, that in a drop or two, the massed army of them seethed almost as if some queer unknown chemical action were in progress rather than an inexplicable mass rhythm of living things.

Those ubiquitous colpidiums described in an earlier chapter were present in legions also, and, as far as I could tell, those from this remote mountain in the ocean were just like the ones found in puddle or pond or the infused vegetation from my own back yard in South Norwalk, Connecticut. They acted just the same, accomplished the same endless movements, and when I stopped to realize that they were living in millions of these bromeliads, maybe in all of the bromeliads in the West Indies and in all of those growing in the entire Amazonian belt of rain forests in South America, the possibility struck that same deep chord of wonder in me once more. How did the ancestors of these creatures get there in the first place? By winds? From the raindrops? We do not know.

The colpidiums were not the only other inhabitants in the vials. They yielded infusorians of several other kinds, a few rotifers, animated algal cells, and an unidentified fauna and flora in the making. How right was that person who wrote: "Evolution has implied the mastery of every possible environment of life."

Part 2. Colombia

"In the depths of the gorge the scene was one of pure enchantment. The lush vegetation grew tangled in the shade, dripping and reveling in the perpetual deluge. The water from above, pulverized to dust in its fall, came down like a torrent of rain, a rush of furious disheveled drops. It collected below, foaming fiercely in the basin it had hollowed in the rock smoothed by the patient hand of ages; and then danced away in the stream again, pursuing its way under the greenery."

Upon reading these lush sentences written by Pierre Loti, I was instantly transported back to South America, to the Eastern Andean country of Colombia, where in a remote rain pocket I found what I believed to be one of the most exquisitely exciting and beautiful places in the world. I found it because I was walking from Sibaté on the *sabana* of Bogotá, by the only mule trail which then led over these Andean spurs to the little coffee-growing town of Fusugasugá, as a member of an American Museum expedition, with the late Dr. Frank M. Chapman as leader, and George K. Cherrie, Thomas M. Ring, Geoffrey O'Connell, and Louis Agassiz Fuertes, beloved friend to whose memory my book is dedicated, as the other members of the group. The others were on foot or on mules; I lingered behind and came upon this bit of paradise where Cherrie and I lived afterwards for many days.

It was an all-day hike from Sibaté on the plain. Reaching the pass at 9600 feet called El Peñon, I started the welcome descent again almost at once. In the cold, wind-swept pass the vegetation was moss grown and stunted, but a short distance below, a marvelous change was abruptly apparent, caused by warm currents rising from the valley to the cooler altitudes. Heavy precipitation was the inevitable result, and thus I came suddenly into a luxuriant high rain forest. Within a short time birds became numerous, most of which were absent or seldom seen higher up. Tall trees laced with lianas and grown with epiphytes lined the lower trail, flowers bloomed in the thicker lower growth, while splendid butterflies drank in crowds around every trail-side puddle.

A little old woman, wrinkled and bent, gave Cherrie and me a room in her windowless hut. One of our doors opened into a pigpen where a fat sow wallowed in the mud, the other into the woman's room through which we had to pass to get out. The floor was earth, the beds just boards, and our clothing and shoes were wet most of the time, but the hut was in this pocket in the wilderness close to a wild stream which plunged down its center from high up above, with the virgin forest growing from its very banks and clinging to the sides of this emerald "V" in the mountains. This was the beginning of the rainy season in March and the periodic showers fell in dense noisy sheets upon the bobbing and dancing foliage. Periodically it would let up suddenly, the clouds would break away and clear hot sunshine would bear down. At once one side of the soaking ravine would be cast into shadow of the densest green, contrasting sharply with the emerald and almost golden hues of the sunny side, from which curls of vapor would appear and rise slowly almost as the sky turned to blue.

Here in this rain pocket we had all of the ingredients necessary to produce and support an endless parade of living things. Indeed there was enough material here for years of study, but we only had time to tarry here and there. At night, lying upon my rough board bed and thankful for my dry air mattress, the call of the stream was like a great magnet. It was a sound of which I never seemed able to hear enough, hypnotizing me sometimes so that I had to get up and go out to sit near by, listening intently as one might to an orchestra. Sitting thus one night, I saw a long row of orange lights like the portholes of a little ship, but glowing upon the ground. They came from strange round organisms filled with cold paste, and when I crushed one in my fingers its life stuff spread upon my skin and caused a part of *me* also to glow with this miracle of heatless light which no one can explain. (Figure 20.) At dawn on the fourth day of our stay I was at the stream bank as usual, and now good fortune brought a new surprise and discovery. Suddenly there came a piercing sound, neither a whistle nor a call note, but more like an urgent shriek. It seemed to come from the whirling waters just below me, startling and astonishing in its clarity above the din of the stream. Then from farther up the watercourse came an answering cry as loud and as penetrating as

Figure 20. A long row of orange lights on the forest floor, like the portholes of a little ship.

the first, and almost as it died away, two diminutive gray-and-white flycatchers * fluttered to each other at midstream, hung there for an instant, then ascended in an aerial caress, and thence to their ball-like nest of bright-green moss suspended from the end of a broken liana.

Here above the foam and spray, these little birds had

---

* *Serpophaga cinerea.*

elected to rear their young, living themselves among the boulders and the shrubs and trees of the stream banks. How many centuries, I wondered, must their kind have lived thus in order to evolve voices so well adapted, voices so startlingly loud and clear to carry above the roar of mountain rain-carriers? How confident were the birds in their hazardous nesting site. I felt concern for those young birds which must launch themselves soon upon their virgin flights, but doubtless such young flycatchers had been doing this very thing successfully for ages. The little family of gray-and-white birds were indeed gracious threads from the great tapestry.

I was in another naturalist's paradise. The cool spray of mountain water, pure and drinkable just as it was, brushed my face in strange contrast to the warm breath of the surrounding forest when sunlit. Where later in the day the spray was flung upward through a sunbeam, a band of rainbow colors remained suspended. Beyond this, a pair of dippers ran about the boulders, not defiant of the crests of froth, just simply and beautifully at home. Overhead a flock of emerald parakeets winged their way in pairs, traveling from the valley to some favorite tree whose ripening buds or fruits now turned a formerly lonely giant into the daily rendezvous for chattering, squabbling crowds. All things here by day seemed to possess the spirit of the stream. The voices of the birds, their swift movements, their very moods spelled joy and freedom and fearlessness. Utterly remote and forgotten on my part were such things as towns and cities and the turmoil of civilization as I observed and smelled the warm perfumes and riches of this bit of wilderness.

In back of me, an old bridge of long mossy timbers spanned the stream, and from it came strange sounds from time to time. Pushing through the soaking ferns and the other vegetation to a place of vantage beneath it, I made another wonderful discovery, for here, flying back and forth, were hummingbirds carrying food to the young in numerous nests. A colony of hummingbirds! How many other naturalists ever feasted their eyes upon such a spectacle? If they had, I had never heard about it in print or otherwise, and I could hardly believe my eyes. The individual birds had woven their nests of moss and down into the moss upon the aged timbers. They were placed quite close together, and because of this matching material they were, of course, quite hard to distinguish at first.

Too delighted to move on, I sat down in the hollow of a big brown boulder, water-carved through the centuries into a huge inverted imbrex. It was like a huge cupped chair, and from its comfort I watched the hummingbird gathering. Between trips to their nests and young they would rest, perching among the jewelweeds by the stream side where their topaz gorgets sparkled in competition with the orange of the blossoms, and where they preened and squeaked, or darted at one another in fights or in play.

There were giant blue *Morpho* butterflies along this stream also, insects of metallic turquoise on the upper side, dull brown underneath. Some followed the watercourse, bobbing up and down and around obstructions erratically. Most of them were alone, or only rarely followed by another. In such cases they would flit past me in jerky fashion, and then flashes of vivid color farther away among the greens of the forest told of sexual quests still in progress.

I sat there by the bridge or wandered up and down the stream between showers all day, completely forgetting about time or food. Then when the deeper shadows of late afternoon climbed up this forested pocket and the heat of day had lessened, the world about the impassioned stream changed completely in mood. The rainbow band was first to go and only a white spray curtain remained to mark its late abode. Up in the old bridge timbers the hummingbirds now brooded their young, while those still perched among the jewelweeds appeared dull green and gray, and no metallic plumage blazed upon their throats. The little fly-catchers were silent also, and the family of dippers disappeared. The sun had gone from this part of the world, but from beyond the hills it threw its beams upward, these spotlight rays striking the emerald plumage of the parakeets now hurrying to their roosts in the valley.

Blossoms closed here and there. Beneath a big *heliconia* leaf a *Morpho* came to sleep, transformed in repose as it brought its wings up over its body, from a brilliant blue to a smoky brown, and for all the world like a big dead leaf. Running its long coiled tongue out and in a few times, and thus completing its simple toilet, it settled for the night. As the light grew dimmer and the last bird calls died away, a strange hush settled over the creatures of day. Only the music of the tumbling waters remained unchanged. It was the interval when neither the creatures of day or night seemed to be stirring, a time put to use by ants and those lower denizens of the forest who make no distinction between light and darkness.

In a very short time seeing became difficult, for night comes on very rapidly in the tropics. Almost along side of me I felt a gentle rush of air, and startling me a bit, a big bird in soft smoky plumage settled upon a stump not five feet away. I could make out its outlines sufficiently to identify it, and with excitement I realized that I was almost within touching distance of that huge goatsucker called *Nyctibius*, now fully awake and ready for its evening meal of moths and big flying beetles. The bird turned its head this way and that, yawned in a cavernous satisfied manner, as so many kinds of animals do, but paid no attention to me whatever. In the treetops, a rasping chorus of locusts commenced their noises, thus announcing their respective desirability, while the pleasanter, more musical notes of tree frogs occasionally sifted through the insect barrage from the same upper strata of foliage.

A small army of bats now appeared out of the gloom, a flock or family gathering which had been sleeping during the day in a long row beneath a slanting limb. Others now came to join these, apparently from under the bridge where the hummingbirds were nesting. All of these queer creatures —representatives of the only order of mammals in the world with an endowment of organic wings—forthwith took over the watercourse as their feeding ground, whirring back and forth, darting and diving, squeaking a little, turning about, sometimes within inches of my face, until pitch darkness swallowed their movements altogether.

Doubtless the creatures of night were now prowling on every side, and it would have been only wild conjecture on my part to try to say what was actually taking place. I made one mental observation, however. All of these creatures of the humid tropical night which I knew about seemed dull and colorless. The smoky goatsucker, the sooty bats, the dappled locusts, a night monkey which I believe I heard overhead; even the *Morpho* butterfly beneath the *heliconia* leaf was smoky brown in its folded dress of night.

The goatsucker poured forth its strange calls at intervals, and after a time it was answered by a mate somewhere, who said something in goatsucker, and at which the one on the stump departed silently again. I know a nut fell out of the forest. With a series of loud taps, it passed through leaves and branches, like an object in a pinball machine, and my head was the bullseye which it hit and then rolled to a stop at my feet. By coincidence, it too was brown and smoky I later ascertained.

Once there was a splashing noise just audible above the roar of the stream, then a faint animal cry and a growl, a pungent sweet-sour odor for a few seconds, and that was all except for the flashes of enormous luminous beetles which were now upon the wing. A man in the forest at night might be easily persuaded to think this or that, and without a moon or a flashlight, or perhaps occasional lightning to give him instantaneous sights, he is even more inclined to let his imagination take over. Actually he can see very little indeed, and alas, a man has neither the sensitive nose of a wild animal, nor the keenness of senses to distinguish correctly between the sounds which issue from so many different sources. A few sounds he knows; the rest is mystery and it is this which makes the tropical forest so alluring, for it still contains things which *no one has ever seen.*

As night had fallen, I realized as never before the marvelous organic whole which even this little rain pocket with all of its interrelated life represented. A going machine by day, a going machine by night. There were day and night shifts of the creatures of which it was constituted, and the forest and the stream were their working quarters—their factory.

I slept that night in the thatched, mud-walled hut of the old woman again, quickly falling asleep next to the pigpen. Some day I hope to find that same stone imbrex and spend more hours musing by the old timber bridge and this singing stream of sweet mountain water in the Andes.

Part 3. British Guiana

"A man sees the end of nothing; whichever way he looks the wood shuts in, one bough folding with another like the fingers of your hand; and whenever he listens he hears something new—"

Quoted from *The Beach at Falsea*, these words of Stevenson's might well have referred to parts of the jungle of

British Guiana. In this great South American forest, in the very territory of Hudson's *Green Mansions* we shall now look into the haunts and the doings of some of its strange and often inexplicable inmates, encountered first as Research Assistant under William Beebe at Kalacoon, the New York Zoological Society's original research station, and later when it was moved to Kartabo on the Cuyuni River some miles farther inland.

How can I describe the Guiana rain forest and its strange areas of enclosed thick jungle growth? In the immediate vicinity of our tents on the Cuyuni, beyond the areas which had once been cleared, we found a forest which was huge, but open and easily traversed underneath, as it usually is where the largest trees exist. Some of these giants were almost straight-boled, tapering but gradually, and with great spreading crowns of the densest foliage. Others were widely buttressed to hold their enormous weights upright in the sandy undersoil, their upper branches studded and packed with hundreds of epiphytes. So much of the sun's light was shut out by these aged trees that mostly slender individuals and saplings grew beneath them. Some of these were the young of the great ones no doubt, the tallest of them sending out delicate sprays of fresh foliage whose individual leaves here and there caught concentrated shafts of sunlight sifting through the main canopy and, as always in these heavy forests, creating much-sought landing places for butterflies.

Strange as it may seem, only a short distance off one of the trails through this high forest I would find myself facing a dense growth, a typical jungle of somewhat smaller trees, wickedly spined black palms, heavy undergrowth, and hundreds or thousands of ascending or descending lianas of every imaginable diameter, from the merest threads to great ropelike vines, many strangely coiled and twisted at or near the ground level, while still other plants and their air roots

in legions clung or fell from the branches of the occasional
big trees towering above the others. In places all of this
vegetable growth formed an interlaced, all but impenetrable
wall like that described by Stevenson. No one can build an
adequate word picture of such jungle scenes. They must be
experienced to be really comprehended in all of their beauty
and strangeness.

The floor of the forest was always wet. One heard the
daily showers approaching, a strange jungle sound at first
far off, but rising rapidly in volume to a unique and characteristic roar as the water poured down from directly overhead. In such cases you either got soaked, ducked for a
hollow tree if you knew of one near by, or lopped off a few
huge jungle leaves for use as a temporary umbrella.

These daily showers left leaf-lined puddles along our
numerous trails, which we had cut with the aid of convicts
supplied by the government from time to time. Impermanent
as these puddles were, I discovered the most remarkable
living things imaginable which dwelt in them, things which
revealed adaptations of which I had never dreamed. They
made me realize anew how insistently nature has attended
to the population and use of even the most transient and
insignificant appearing habitats; how strange creatures have
inexplicably been evolved as if in order to fit the queerest
and poorest of them.

Truthfully I had expected to find only insect and protozoan life within these puddles, but it always pays to investigate thoroughly. Probing around in one of these miniature
ponds with my tough little net of bolting cloth, I brought
forth eight tiny fishes. They were easily captured, and as it
afterward turned out they were not at all uncommon in the
Guiana forest, exquisite little things, those which I believed
to be the males flushed with pale hues of pink and yellow,
with lighter spots upon their sides, reminding me of minia-

ture trout an inch to an inch and three-quarters in length. These were land minnows, well known to ichthyologists,[*] but excitingly new to me, for here were fishes which, we afterwards proved, could remain out of water if their bodies and gills remained damp, for eight or nine days at a stretch. The vitality of the captives was amazing. They seemed to be quite immune to shock also, even when suddenly and rudely netted and handled, and thus in complete contrast to many much larger species, such for instance, as the spearing of Long Island Sound waters which often die of shock as soon as removed from their medium.

Experimenting with the land minnows, I placed them upon wet leaves some distance from their puddle, and to my astonishment they commenced to flip themselves along energetically, some of them, perhaps only by chance, right back in the direction of the water from which I had just taken them. Many other puddles now examined contained minnows, and it became evident that they can flip along for considerable distances in search of additional water if their first location dries up. Specimens placed in glass jars wriggled up the damp sides of the glass when the oxygen in the water became exhausted, and thus we discovered that they could actually remain out of water for so many days. As these little fishes also inhabited streams within the forest, the question arose, why did other individuals migrate to the puddles in the first place? Possibly they found more suitable breeding conditions away from the running streams, but we really do not know.

From still another of these lucrative trailside puddles I extracted two of the strangest forest amphibians that I had so far laid eyes upon. The bottom of this puddle was littered with leaves and fragments which were black and slimy. In examining wads of this odoriferous debris, I no-

[*] *Rivulus stagnatus.*

ticed a very slight movement of what at first seemed to be a leaf and nothing more, but the closer I inspected this thing, the more incredulous I became, for this bit of "vegetation" proved to be a representative of what must be the thinnest genus of backboned animals in existence. It was a Surinam toad, a species which eventually grows somewhat larger than the inch and a quarter long individuals I had found, and the female of which carries her eggs enclosed in dermal cells upon her back, from which the young emerge.* It did not seem possible that their flat bodies could contain all of the highly developed organs necessary to backboned animals. Indeed their "works" *were* greatly flattened, arranged within them as cleverly as those in a fine Swiss watch. These creatures were so colored and textured upon their exteriors that they exactly matched the water-blackened leaves, while their tiny, untoadlike eyes added to the illusion. In the low and secretive places in which they lived, I wondered what animals hunted them for food. It would seem that they must have serious enemies to have evolved such perfect protective form and coloration.

Finding the land minnows and the Surinam toads seemed ample rewards for a single trail, but now I came upon partly concealed hollows in the leaves which contained masses of what appeared to be beaten up egg white. These pools of mucus froth measured from three to five inches in diameter and two or three inches in depth. Under the upper slippery layers consisting of fine bubbles, a little clear water had collected in each case, and in these hollows swam a number of tadpoles, the young of a species of *Leptodactylus* frog. There are several species which make such remarkable arrangements. I cannot say which one these nests belonged to, nor do I know how the mucus froth is produced. What interested me most was that in this forest where there were of

* *Pipa americana.*

course many frog-eating creatures, still another ingenious measure to protect a small creature had been devised by nature, one in which an amphibian had been shown a method of *building* ponds and screening them with its own remarkable secretions.

The amphibians of the great forest continued to astonish me. I heard a rather sweet-toned call one day which may have come from a small blackish-brown frog with orange-red stripes upon its thighs. Upon looking at the forest floor in the direction from which the sound apparently had issued, I saw this creature and soon had it in my hand, a nursing frog * carrying a mob of living tadpoles clustered upon its moist back and thighs. Here was the *male* of the species carrying the babies, of all things, a trait of this genus, the reason for which no one knows.

Squatting Indian style one day in the shadow of a huge, buttressed tree, and holding a few big philodendron leaves up in front of me for camouflage, I was watching to see what might come my way. A pair of ant-thrushes sang back and forth to each other and some other small birds called and "chipped" as they followed a mass of driver ants not far away. These, and the sound of an occasional falling leaf or nut dropping through the branches to the forest floor, were all that disturbed the woodland silence. A few minutes passed thus uneventfully, then into the higher branches overhead swooped a clumsy, noisy group of big toucans. With their huge brightly colored bills they commenced to pull at the purplish-blue fruit clusters with which the big tree was loaded and which I had not even noticed before the birds' arrival. This was good! I had happened to squat this time directly beneath an ideal lure in the vast forest, and upon looking more carefully at the ground around me

* A species of *Dendrobates*.

I saw that it too was littered with chewed fruit which had already been knocked down.

The toucans fed copiously, picking each berry carefully and then tossing it neatly into their throats. After eating, they would hop to a soaking spongy root mass of some aerial plant, and squeezing it in their strong beaks, produce water, which they drank with the aid of their long, feathered tongues. Other birds now came into the food tree—pale-gray and blue tanagers, silver-beaked tanagers, and two pairs of a species of Amazon parrot. All at once there was a commotion among the higher branches and foliage; most of the birds departed abruptly, the parrots with raucous shrieks, and there where it had evidently been all the while was a big weasel-like animal, a gallictus,* a long-tailed musteline mammal allied to the grison.

A gallictus measures three feet in length. It has a squarish gray head and short black hair elsewhere. This one progressed among the high limbs with ease and assurance, its tail held out straight behind as I watched fascinated as only one can be upon seeing a wild animal new to one for the first time. It would reach out for the fruits with its paws, drawing in the smaller branches and then plucking the berries with its mouth. The hard interior seeds were uneaten and kept falling about me, and occasionally a bitten or untouched fruit about the size of a cranberry fell also. Examining one of these I found it to be soft and slightly sweet and rather pleasant tasting, but what this fruit is called I do not know.

Suddenly there came loud angry growls accompanied by a veritable shower of green and ripe berries. Looking up excitedly I saw a second gallictus advancing upon the first one who now returned these snarling insults which caused number two to stop short and nonchalantly commence feed-

* *Tayra barbara barbara.*

ing again. Alternately now the two mammals endeavored to intimidate each other, growling, staring, and stuffing themselves meanwhile. Gradually they came closer and closer together and I expected to witness a grand battle from a grandstand seat, but nothing further happened. Instead of fighting, number two withdrew, and to my amazement came down the big tree trunk with the ease of a squirrel, head first, to within three feet of me, where, suddenly sensing me, it jumped to the ground and made off with all haste.

This food tree lured at least four species of monkeys, peccaries and agoutis and tyras by day, and it was thrilling to realize that jaguars and pumas doubtless stalked their prey here at night, wonderful to realize that none of these wild creatures would bother us as we examined their realm.

Once in a while a huge metallic-blue wasp with coppery red wings would alight in the trail. Flipping its wings up and down periodically as it walked over the dead leaves, it would examine every niche and crevice with its sensitive curled antennae. It was searching for a large species of spider, which if encountered would be stung into unconsciousness and dragged to a previously prepared burrow. Here an egg would be attached to the victim's body and the young wasp upon hatching would thus have ample food to bring it to maturity. This, with many variations as to the kind of victim sought, is the typical procedure of solitary wasps in general.

On one day an insect which had been netted, and which I believed to be one of these big wasps, proved upon closer examination to be an entirely different insect. It was the same length as the wasp and it was equipped with the same sort of long blue legs supporting its body well above the ground. Its color pattern was the same, even to the coppery wings folded flat upon its body, and its curling, bicolored antennae. Even its compound eyes were similar, but unlike the wasp there were three erect spikes upon the newcomer's back, and its mouthparts consisted of a wicked-looking, back-turned beak or scimitar which placed the creature among the reduviidae or assassin bugs, far removed from the order to which the wasp belonged.

From a short distance, when alive this insect could be immediately mistaken for the wasp, not only because of its form and color, but because of its identical nervous, wing-flipping motions. At first glance it would seem to be a "mimic" without a doubt, a bug gaining protection through its close resemblance to the stinging wasp, but a little further analysis negated such an explanation. With a tremendous stinging beak of its own with which it could inflict excruciatingly painful wounds on a man, and death on its small natural food animals, it would need no such secondary protection. The bug was not "mimicking" *anything*. In this case nature had not copied a wasp in the form of a bug. It was probably a case of parallelism, something for which in this case there would seem to be no other explanation.

Nights at Kartabo beneath great clumps of bamboo were delightfully peaceful. There were sounds of course, like the strange creakings and rattling of these hollow-joined trees when the wind stirs them. There were the crescendos of approaching showers and the occasional soul-filling choruses of troops of howling monkeys. No matter how many times I had heard them previously, a definite shiver would course up and down my spine, not a shiver of innate fear, but the same sort of uncontrollable something which engulfs one when a fine military band comes blaring into sight and hearing.

These monkeys of the Guiana forest were huge bearded creatures, with golden-red fur, powerful limbs, and prehensile tails, equipment which for some unexplained reason seems to be peculiar to New World monkeys. Their large mouths and teeth were variously stained by the juices of fruits and seeds, and the throats of the males especially were greatly enlarged. In skinning specimens collected for a group in the American Museum of Natural History, we examined the cause of these swellings—the double sound-boxes into which the thyroid cartilage has evolved. These objects were actually enormously exaggerated Adam's apples which acted as sounding boards for the great voices of these mammals. One of the sound-boxes, which I have before me as I write, would about fill my hand, and its peculiar shape and attachments would be difficult to describe. (Figure 21.)

I do not know just why they howl as they do at various times, except of course when one troop approaches too closely to the chosen territory of another. In any case, these concerts commenced with low undistinguished grunting, growling sounds, which, however, grew louder and louder and more splendid, punctuated with great gasps between successive roars, the mammals apparently urging themselves on and on to greater and more tremendous effects which literally cause their treetop domains to tremble, and which in actual volume I believe outclasses even the roars of lions. Anyone who has not heard these monkeys in the wild cannot imagine the full majesty of the sounds. Regardless of what other authors may have said to the contrary, it definitely seemed to me that rain brought forth the loudest protestations.

Aside from these intriguing aural treats and many other strange vibrations which were born of the rain forest, there were the odors of the day and the night to claim one's frequent attention. Odors are ubiquitous in the tropics, strange new ones and partly or wholly familiar ones as well. They are important long after a trip has ended in helping to recall more vividly particular forest scenes and atmospheres. There were the strong or sweetish odors of animals which drifted to one and quickly passed. There was the characteristic odor left by howler troops in their dung beneath their sleeping-trees, not offensive, and often a way of locating hiding silent bands during the heat of midday. There were powerful musky smells, and the deeply repelling stink—the only ade-

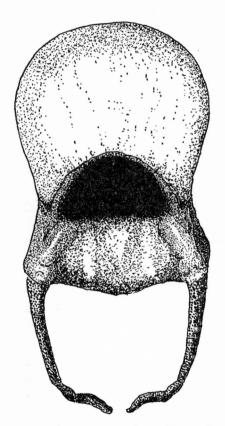

Figure 21. The hollow cartilaginous sound-amplifying device from the throat of a big male red howling monkey collected by the author in British Guiana. Drawn exactly life size.

quate word describing it—which issued from the beautiful lacelike stalks of a jungle fungus. There were smells akin to those of wet and recently fallen oak leaves and newly cut maple logs blended with fermenting sap, but whose actual sources were never identified. There were odors thrown out from oozing red-and-orange gums and resinous tree wounds, substances which had enmeshed flies and other insects, just as amber in its liquid youth had caught insects millions of years ago. There were the opening buds and flowers releasing aromatic essential oils in infinitesimal droplets, as sweet and as dense as rhodium, and evaporating terpenes whose gaseous components, blending with other and unknown volatile essences of the jungle air, may have caused some of the little curls of haze, visible only to a sensitive observer, and which disappeared again almost as they were discovered against the deep greens and browns of the moist forest. All of these strange, familiar, or scarcely discernible scents, drifting singly or in sympathetic chains, were phases of the jungle which became locked forever, indelibly in one's memory as if in hardened crystal plastic.

I left my tent one night when howlers were bellowing with all their might. I sat down at the end of our little pier which jutted out into the Cuyuni River. Looking up and about me I let my imagination wander happily, in the heavens, upon the dark river water, and upon the dimly outlined jungle walls. Of these billions of suns or stars overhead, of those trillions of organisms in the great stream in front of me and in the almost endless forest at my back, I understood so very little, yet this was doubtless what so filled me with inspiration. I thought of those who regularly pass by all such things (would pass by all for instance which I have gathered into this book) as commonplace automatic objects and happenings, things to be cut up in the laboratory into easily understood and recognizable packets like identical boxes of wedding cake. I felt sorry for these people, for when one no longer responds to a sense of awe and wonder in the world, even in regard to the tiny entities as well as the stars, the soul has commenced to wither and die.

The monkey choruses, one on each side of the Cuyuni, interrupted my thoughts. To me the voices sounded exactly alike, and what they were trying to convey had doubtless been so for centuries without change. Like all of the other mammals inhabiting the earth except ourselves, these howlers had never achieved the power of relating anything really important in words. There was no such thing as conversation or the latest distant gossip. The interchange of ideas or the learning of others would never be theirs to accumulate at will. They illustrated graphically the enormous chasm existing between men and all of these other species. There they were over there in the wet uncomfortable treetops, all free to be sure, but only able to growl and grunt and bark and howl into the night, not exchanging even the simpler ideas which might improve their lot; without a single thought which their great, great, great, ad infinitum, grandparents had not thought hundreds or thousands of years before them. Unable to improve their standard of living an iota, they would go right on eating the same old foods, breeding, and howling through life, static, and all but abandoned mentally.

How very different our own case. How wonderful to be able to store up in a single lifetime in a single brain, if we apply it, much of the handed-down knowledge of the past. How fortunate that over and over again accompanying conscious thought came faith and assurance that our experience here on earth is not the end of experience.

Contrasting my lot that night under the South American stars, and ever since, with that of the red howlers, as a symbol perhaps of about the best that the *other* animals may hope for and still remain free, I felt a warm and grateful glow, a deep satisfaction that I was born a seeing, feeling, conscious human being with this sense of wonder, gratitude, and humility.

Part 4.   Panama

It was with Frank M. Chapman, long Curator of Birds at the American Museum of Natural History, Louis Agassiz Fuertes, the great bird artist, George K. Cherrie, veteran explorer, Thomas M. Ring, and Geoffrey O'Connell that I first set foot in Panama. This was back in January, 1913. As one of the museum's expeditions we were headed for the eastern base of the Eastern Andes and the great Llanos or "prairies" of Colombia.* At that time Gatun Dam was still under construction, and what is now Barro Colorado Island in Gatun Lake was but another Panama hilltop covered with virgin forest growth. Years later, Chapman made Barro Colorado Island his winter headquarters and there he wrote his famous "Air Castle" books regarding the wildlife, which, however, was some time after he and Dr. James Zatek and the late Dr. Thomas Barbour of Harvard's Museum of Comparative Zoology had pioneered there, the latter naturalists having been responsible in 1923 for the actual coming into being of this Canal Zone Biological Area as the island sanctuary which is now owned and maintained by the Smithsonian Institution is called. Accredited scientists and naturalists from all over the world have been welcome to study there, and I often wonder now, if Chapman even imagined way back there in 1913, as we stopped for a day or so on our way to South America, that one day he would return to

* Dr. Chapman, Fuertes, and Cherrie have already passed on. For details of this Colombian journey see *The Bulletin of the Massachusetts Audubon Society*, Vol. XLI, Nos. 8 and 9, 1957, and Vol. XLII, Nos. 1, 2, and 3, 1958.

this very hilltop and there institute a dozen seasons of distinguished study and literary accomplishment. It would indeed be interesting to know.

Forty-four years after my first visit, my wife and I spent
the winter of 1957 within two minutes' walk of the little
house which Chapman had built for himself at Barro Colorado, a sanctum which he loved as he loved the whole island
and the splendid forest which began almost at his door.
I sat down in his little house many times during our stay. I
studied the now vacant rooms where he had slept, where
he had written his books, indeed where he had spent some
of his happiest days, and here it seemed to me that Chapman
was always present in spirit, so closely had I associated this
particular spot with his later life. There were the shelves
where for each season's work he had kept his cameras, his
binoculars, and his library, as described in his books. There
was his name or part of it, crudely scratched into the cement
of one of the concrete steps leading to the wooden ones and
his door. On the forest side of the dwelling stood the same
big balsa tree in which he had observed the birds and the
monkeys. In February we found it in full flower and its
deep, creamy, five-inch blossoms were still being carefully
opened and peeked into by the white-faced monkeys * just
as Chapman had written about them from the very observation spot upon which I stood. The clearing and the high
forest were there too, almost unchanged. With a keen sense
of nostalgia I recalled the long ride over the Andes with
Chapman in 1913, a time when there were no automobiles
even in the capital of Bogatá. I recalled the long wet days
of collecting and in the saddle, and sleeping wherever we
might be; the severe intermittent fever we both contracted;
but most of all I remembered the great collection of birds
and mammals which we made, and the high spots of those

* *Cebus capucinus imitator.* Called *cariblanco* by the natives.

field days which we six men spent in a primitive country.

Today, CHAPMAN HOUSE (it bears a little sign like that) stood vacant. Its door slammed back and forth in the Trade Wind breezes. Someone who cared nothing for his memory had left it open and banging. I went up the well-worn wooden steps from the cement walk and closed it, turned around, looked up, and there in the same big jacaranda tree,* now flowering like a giant bouquet of violets, dangled the great woven nests of a colony of chestnut-headed oropéndolas, the homes of these big brown and black and yellow orioles † in many stages of construction, and the completed tapering baglike structures measuring forty or more inches in length. Probably no one could have said with accuracy how many birds constituted this colony, the females seemed to be in excess, and a single male is known to breed with more than one individual. Chapman studied the entire life history of this species at Barro Colorado and chronicled the facts in his articles and books. In one of the "Air Castle" volumes he also told of the visits of the white-faced monkeys to the big balsa tree, and how they poked their heads into the depths of the great buds as though they might just be smelling them. I found, however, that they were actually parting the flower petals for the purpose of reaching pools of nectar which lay in the bases of these blossoms. The significant fact was that these usually careless monkeys did not injure the balsa flowers as they often injure and waste other kinds of vegetation when feeding. They have learned, as I did, that this nectar supply sometimes replenishes itself. When placed in water promptly, blossoms with short stems, which I was able to secure, secreted additional fluid after their original offering had been removed with a hypodermic syringe. One blossom's offerings

---

* *Jacaranda j. copaia.* The balsa mentioned above is *Ochroma copaifera.*
† *Zarhynchus wagleri ridgwayi.*

suggested the probability that those upon the tree secrete nectar for several days, which would account for the repeated visits of the monkeys and the care with which they part the flower petals.

Every trip along the numerous older trails on rocky, hilly, root-grown Barro Colorado assures interesting and unexpected sights and sounds in a splendid tropical forest. It was strange also to come unexpectedly upon great vivid patches of violet or pink, yellow or white illuminating the normally brown leafy carpet of the forest floor, something which would occur with remarkable suddenness when after the short blooming periods of these flowering trees, all of their blossoms or petals tumbled pell-mell to the ground.

For all the interest of these older trails, and the new narrow ones which I marked out very faintly for my exclusive use, the most rewarding hours were spent sitting near, or quietly traversing the bed of a trickling brooklet which wound its way up and down through a defile in the big forest—up toward the top of the steep island where it finally vanished into the ground—down around many a bend to Gatun Lake far below. Often I would walk the stream bed on the moist brown rocks, stealthily advancing a few steps at a time, then stopping to look and listen before continuing again. This was always exciting, especially when rounding a little bend or sneaking past huge rocks or ducking under screens and barriers of fallen limbs and underbrush. At other times I sat motionless for long periods just to observe the intriguing drama and the living things which were sure to show up sooner or later, and ignore me, usually, because of my green shirt and khaki trousers which blended nicely with the surrounding rocks and the forest. For at least a part of fifty-nine days I did just these two things, and this final chapter will be made up mostly of what I found and observed along this little watercourse.

I was intrigued always by the gurgling, watery, or un-
earthly utterances of the big male oropéndolos which
dropped down through the forest to the brook bed to drink.
Normally birds of the sunny branches of the treetops where
they nested, they seemed nevertheless to fit in here very
well, their vascular voices blending with that of the brooklet,
in the humid, often motionless air of the defile. They plopped
and gurgled from somewhere within their anatomies, drank
copiously, and when alarmed made off with rattling grating
calls toward the nesting colony not far away, where strange
routines and other strange sounds accompanied nest-building,
to me inexplicable goings-on despite the simplification written into such actions by the behaviorists.

Under a dark overhanging bank near where I sat each
day, a pair of tiny ruddy-tailed flycatchers * selected a thin
hanging root upon which to weave their incredibly neat and
beautiful ball-like nest, with its conical dome roof, in which
the trusting female, after initial indecision at my presence
each day, laid three pure-white eggs which were gobbled
up as legitimate jungle fare by some other creature as soon
as the set was complete.

At three black tunnels, left by the roots of a huge tree
which had long ago fallen down the slope of the ravine, a
pair of rufous motmots † considered these dark holes as
places correct for baby-raising. Seventeen inches in length,
chestnut and green, turquoise and violet blue, these strange
and beautiful birds for some unknown reason are believed
to pluck out portions of their very long tail feathers, thus
leaving characteristic racket-shaped tips with sections of
bare shaft in between. Do they actually do it themselves and
if so why? We do not know.

* *Terenotriccus erythrurus fulvigularis.*
† *Baryphthengus ruficapillus semirufus.*

On my first sitting occasion at the stream, two strange insects happened my way. One was a small mantis, the other a minute fly which came to rest upon a leaf. Even with my unaided eyes I could see that this mantis and this fly were peculiar. The fly seemed to have some foreign object stuck crosswise where the front of its head should have appeared round. It looked as a large animal might, were it carrying a five-foot section of tree trunk where its mouth should be. The mantis's head was peculiar also, like the head of a pin with large shining beads glued to it. Here were two insects which would bear examination so I collected them both and later placed them under the microscope. Now the mantis's eyes became two nearly perfect globes out of all proportion to the owner's head. Each globe was studded with more than a hundred facets, dashed here and there with wedges of violet organic paint. They looked like huge glass balls bound neatly with tight-fitting Brussels netting, and bulging from the head on a giraffelike neck. That this creature's eyes had been designed for panoramic vision was obvious at a glance. There were facets which pointed in every direction and saw in every direction without the necessity of the eyes or the head being moved at all. Here was a pair of organic binoculars, superior in the *field* which they covered, to those manufactured by man, true instruments of survival.

The tiny fly was even more astonishing, for the microscope revealed that what had been mistaken for a foreign object adhering to its head, was instead its *entire* head, connected to the rest of its body by a neck no thicker than a horse hair. The entire head was in the form of a tube, by itself longer than the insect's entire body. On the lower side of this tube in front, a bristled tongue protruded from a round well, while the tube proper was drawn out, graduating into amazing faceted compound eyes at the end of elongated nipples, and striped with red and brilliant blue. I had never seen anything like this, a head designed of course for some very special purpose or mode of existence. Your guess as to its reason and function is as good as mine. (Figure 22.)

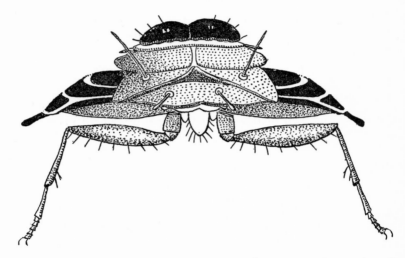

Figure 22. The head of a minute fly from the Panama forest viewed from the front and enlarged about eighteen times. The purpose of this specialized equipment is anybody's guess. The eyes proper are the striped object with nipplelike tips.

On some days in March or early April, when the trade winds ceased to blow, the air down in the stream bed became close and heavy. The brown rocks and I sweated even though motionless. Through this dim abode, where twilight seemed to come earlier than anywhere else in the forest, black-yellow-and-brown butterflies drifted languidly upon weak elongated wings.*

---

* *Mechanitis isthmea.*

These could be caught almost without effort, in direct contrast to that which had to be expended upon tiny, darting, but gorgeous blue, black, and violet-winged Lycaenids which also inhabited the banks of the stream bed, flitting in among the rocks and taking moisture therefrom. Still other strange butterflies whose flight was so fast the eye could scarcely follow them sometimes darted up and down the watercourse, disappearing almost as they were discovered, as they folded themselves upon some matching tree.

During the brightest hours when the sun was high over the forest, those huge metallic azure *Morpho* butterflies came out of hiding to delight my eyes and whet my inborn collector's appetite, some measuring five inches across their expanded forewings, and ten times the size of some of the Lycaenids. The stream bed was their regular flyway. I could almost always net them there. Periodically I would see alternate flashes of vivid blue and all but disappearing dabs of ocher-brown, indicating the upper and lower wing surfaces of these wonderful insects in their dodging or drifting courses. Sometimes they came to rest upon the trunks of saplings not far above the water, then closing their wings tightly together over their backs and thus shutting out every hint of blue, they became big dead leaves almost in an instant. Still other individuals descended to the partly choked places in the stream where almendro nuts dropped by the monkeys and coatis from far above fermented an odd-smelling brew which the morphos drank avidly. At such times, again with their wings held upright and folded, their brown camouflage was truly extraordinary, especially in the case of a common banded species.

At such drinking sprees, like certain leaf-patterned forest toads, the butterflies were in some manner cognizant of their protective coloring, for they sometimes failed to fly off until nearly trod upon. No one knows how both butterflies and moths are often able to select leaves or bark or other substances which blend protectively with their own patterns. As we have seen in this book, *Catocala* moths in New England seem to become part of the bark upon which they rest; morphos turn into either pale or dark-brown dead leaves, and there were other butterflies on Barro Colorado Island which persistently selected gray-mottled tree trunks, the lichen-dappled, cement water-storage tank, and the flecked-gray steel of the observation tower as their efficiently obliterating resting places.*

Long before this Panama sojourn, I had learned in British Guiana to lure morphos by placing the wings of a dead one in my hatband. I now used another trick with great success. From a battered specimen, I removed the four wings and cemented them in natural spread positions upon a sheet of Bristol board, upon which I had first painted the head and body in India ink. The object was then carefully cut out with the scissors and covered with protective cellophane. This became my decoy. Balanced by four black shoe threads and suspended by a single long thread from a twig near the stream bed, or in any other well-used flyway such as a trail or the swath made by a fallen tree, this thing would bob and turn and flash blue in the slightest breeze. Morphos were lured by it time and again. Never, in my experience, however, did one actually stop at such a decoy. Fifty per cent or more of these wanderers which saw it flash were attracted toward it, some to hesitate for an instant, or to make a single turn about the fake before making off upon their erratic journeys once more. The trick allowed just time enough for one or two rapid net swings and an occasional capture of the prize.

Keeping down close to the dead leaf carpet of the forest floor, and barely discernible for two quite different reasons,

* *Argeronia feronia.*

were two other butterflies whose movements were like the passage of indistinct small shadows. The first of these,* had two-and-one-half-inch wings, whose subtle shades and angular shapes made color union with many a fallen leaf in the insect's dim habitats, and whose darkened diagonal lines represented the mid-ribs and veins of the leaves, thus adding to the illusion when at rest. Amazing as this creature's protective coloration was, it was understandable, and one could easily imagine how through the centuries natural selection had screened out the less protective variations from perhaps tens of thousands of generations.

Under the microscope this butterfly's wings were seen to be well clothed with thousands upon thousands of minute scales, some flattened and placed row after row as neatly as shingles upon the roof of a modern dwelling. The scales were especially thick and numerous where they produced dark eye-spots with white "pupils" upon the hind wings. The diagonal bands and remaining patterns were well sprinkled with longer, much narrower black scales in addition to the flat shinglelike ones below. Here upon these wings, in microscopic units and in enormous quantity, was the material for selection, from which the wonderfully protective pattern which we see today had been evolved.

The somewhat smaller of the two inhabitants of this same domain down upon the leaf carpet of the forest, flying daintily but a few inches above it, was the species which for convenience I called the enigma butterfly.† Except for sparse brown bands, black-and-white eye-spots and delicate reddish areas along the lower edges of the hind wings, this insect was almost scaleless, transparent, and the color of pale consommé. In place of the conventional scales, the

* *Pierella luna.*
† *Callitaera menander.*

microscope revealed the most delicate hairs, each one distinct and evenly set apart from the next.

When this butterfly was in flight or at rest, most of the visible color was that of the dead leaves showing through its wings from beneath, and the question which arose in my mind was how this scale-loosing process could have been initiated and then carried on as an evolutionary measure of survival. Here were two butterfly species living side by side in an identical environment and protected in opposite ways; one patterned with an exquisite tapestry of scales, the other well on the way to being minus any scales at all.

Strange to say, we soon found out that even some of the mosquitoes which lived down along the brooklet were extraordinary. They did not bite for one thing, and under the microscope in some cases they were truly startling. The shimmering silver and blue shades of their bodies were like the colors in gorgeous jewelry. From what we might popularly refer to as their "knee joints" on their forelegs grew massed plumes, prismatic in silver and violet, magenta and blue, the plumes forming two elaborate flattened fans, one below the other upon each leg, and each made up of at least five hundred feathery units surrounding each purple support. Often attracted to me, these creatures moved upon enormously long, enormously stiltlike legs shingled with hundreds of blue and violet scales. They carried blunt beaks, and antennae like elaborate television aerials, and they flew about on elongate smoky wings, which, as indicated by the very high-pitched sounds they produced, must have vibrated at enormous speeds.

In the presence of such designs and such wonderful magnification of their details, I realized anew of how much our normal vision leaves us in ignorance, and what marvelous sights we overlook on every side. One could forget easily enough that these were naught but mosquitoes which I had beneath my lenses, and it is doubtful if anyone knows for certain the uses which all of their elaborate leg equipment serves. How drab by comparison are the costumes and equipment of many animals which appear large to our un-aided eyes. How far away is our profoundest guess about the cell formulae which have brought these threads of the great tapestry into living being.

Tens of thousands of army ants came down the stream bed one late afternoon, where I watched them for hours. The insect legions were moving rather slowly in this case, divided into a number of comparatively narrow columns, rather than in those massed bulges whose impetus at the extreme front seems to come as much from the pressure of those advancing at the rear as it does from any great enthu-siasm of those in the lead to advance. Doubtless this army had recently left one of their periodic bivouacs which last nineteen days, during which the young or larval ants spin their cocoons prior to transforming into adults, and the queen lays thousands of eggs to insure the next generation. With emergence of the young adults from the cocoons, the army marches once more for seventeen days, foraging on the way before the next bivouac again. This, I believe, is the normal cycle of ants of the genus *Eciton* which I was ob-serving.

Ants are one of evolution's oldest and most successful families. Indications of their presence on earth sixty-five mil-lion years ago have been recorded in early Jurassic fossils. In the opening chapter of this book I spoke of evolution's satisfactory inventions which have remained static by the wayside, or almost so, for X-million years. The ant is one of these, and had there been intelligent human beings living millions of years ago, they doubtless could have observed some of the same ant habits which astonish us today. Indeed, in musing thus as the army came close, I felt very immature, face to face with such a venerable race of creatures.

Ant shrikes, puffbirds, and broad-billed motmots, all forest-loving birds,* advanced in short flights ahead of the army. Again and again they swooped down in front of the columns, coming up in some cases with big kicking wood roaches, but more often with those fast-moving, long-legged rock spiders which, at the first ominous rustling sound that seemed to telegraph itself through the leaves of the forest floor from the countless moving feet of the approaching hordes, made quick panicky leaps in any direction away from their hiding places. The motmots were by far the most expert, securing many of the spiders and bearing them off to safe perches where they devoured them at once. If the spiders were not snatched by the birds, they were soon outflanked by the ants. One or two would at last fasten their mandibles upon a spider's leg, only to be born aloft at once as the terrified creature tried to escape, jumping wildly here and there. Each time the victim touched the ground, additional ants would clamp upon it, until the ever increasing weight would anchor the poor thing; then, horrible to witness, its body would instantly shrivel under a milling mob of bodies and gnashing jaws as if it might have been caught in a violent withering fire.

Every crack and crevice along the stream bed, every space beneath the stones and rocks, every low-growing stem and leaf of the shrubbery was violently searched. These ants somehow reminded me of human soldiers with flame-throwers driving out every terrified living thing in their paths. Some ants were carrying parts torn from other insects

---

* *Thamnophilus punctatus atrinucha, Notharcus macrorhynchus hyperrhynchus,* and *Electron platyrhynchus minor.*

and spiders; others had whole red amphipod crustaceans resembling small sand-hoppers which may have been as tasty to ants as fat fresh shrimps are delicious to us.

A gorgeous frog with glistening black body and blue-green markings was now routed out but escaped; * this was the so-called "poisonous" frog which however, is incapable of killing even small animals.[2,3]

Next I was astonished to see a huge black creature called a tailless whip scorpion, belonging to the family Tarantulidae, also routed from its lair. It is an arachnid with legs several inches in length, a wide, flat body, and great incurved claws lined with rows of inturned spikes for holding its prey.

Undaunted by its size, a few ants grabbed its longest horsehairlike appendages and hanging on desperately they braced their feet against small stones, tugging and straining backwards at an angle exactly as men might do if trying to hold a rhinoceros or a dinosaur at the end of two slender ropes. The scorpion tried with all its strength to progress backwards, but more and more ants came to the assistance of the first ones. Still others rushed to the rear and pushed the struggling victim forward, then in another instant it was swarmed over and would have been quickly rent asunder had I not intervened and collected this monstrosity for myself. With its legs spread out the whip scorpion is fully as wide as my hand, a really horrid-looking beast which I should think might have frightened even an army ant.

As long as I watched this army it did not spread out very much. My method was to move to a position a yard or so in front of the columns, sit down, and there observe the complete rout of the normally hidden fauna of the forest floor. Thus, retreating gradually backwards as the leading

* *Dendrobates tinctorius.*

ants approached, and in no danger whatever, I greatly enjoyed watching the whole spectacle.

Near the rear of the army a few stragglers stumbled along
bearing various items. One of these had obtained a whole
wing of a big forest damselfly, a creature resembling a delicately built dragonfly or "darning needle," whose head is
mostly two big compound eyes, and whose body is almost
as slender as a broom straw. I wondered how this insect had
allowed itself to be caught and dismembered of its five-inch
wings, for damselflies are alert and almost constantly in
flight.

After studying the habits of the three common species of
these insects, I preferred to call forest damselflies by the
more appropriate name of "damselcopters," for in flight their
four elegant, shimmering, slowly fluttering wings produced
a striking illusion of tiny rotors in motion. They rose rapidly
or descended slowly; they turned abruptly, swung back
upon their courses, or hovered in one spot like maneuvering
whirlybirds. It was soon discovered that these insects were
feeding themselves by robbing the webs of very small
spiders. Drifting slowly up and down in front of the silken
orbs, which were common in the forest attached to dead
twigs, they neatly plucked out the smallest of the entangled
gnats or other minute things that were apparently beneath
the notice of the unprotesting spider builders. Thus the
"damselcopters" were taking advantage of ready-trapped
game and keeping the webs partly cleared in the act. Might
this possibly be the dawn of another case of symbiosis, a
case in the making? Again we do not know.

Near the spot where the ruddy-tailed flycatchers had had
their nest, I established my favorite watching post. Here at
some remote time two huge rocks had been lodged so close
together that now the brooklet and I had just room to pass
between them. More recently, a tall tree had fallen in such

a way that it formed a gently inclined bridge across the top of the rocks. The old trunk was mostly hidden in a lush coat of mosses and ferns and epiphytes, as were the dim black banks into which the boulders merged. Shafts of yellowish light angled down from openings in the forest canopy, striking individual leaves and forming favored sunning places for wandering butterflies. Advancing charmed through this dark natural tunnel each sunny day to the filtered luminous light beyond, I would find my accustomed seat upon a smaller rock from which I could watch a portion of the brook in both directions. I could see dozens of little fish within it, watch tiny black frogs among the stones, and I could also scan the forest arc high overhead, the abode of toucans, crested guans, white-faced capuchin monkeys, and black howlers.*

From high up in the taller forest and passing through the leafy lace of saplings which had sprung up through the wreckage of a long-fallen giant tree came a certain shaft of sunlight for a while on each fair morning. Fortunately, for nearly a month this one brilliant beam thus spotlighted a little group of buds and flowers at the end of a dangling vine only six feet above the forest floor. Far above this illuminated bouquet, another, larger vine had climbed along a tree trunk well into the brilliant open sunlight. There it had come into full bloom and its masses of pink blossoms now lured not only gorgeous swallowtail butterflies, but the forest hummingbirds of several species. Periodically, individual hummers dipped down from the big vine which was prolific of nectar and insects to sip at the lesser offerings of the suspended blooms below.

One of my trails led up through the thick vegetation of

* Keel-billed toucan, *Ramphastos sulfuratus brevicarinatus.* Swainson's toucan, *R. swainsonii.* Crested guan, *Penelope purpurascens aequatorialis.* White-faced monkey, *Cebus capucinus imitator.* Black howler, *Alouatta palliata aequatorialis.*

the hillside, from the brook to this hummingbird lure. By leveling off a bit of the ground close by for the tripod, and by lopping off a big leaf or two which blocked the Bolex camera, I succeeded, after long hours of waiting, in obtaining color sequences of the long-tailed and little hermit hummingbirds, and that photogenic creature known as the Colombian wood nymph, a hummer bedecked in varying shades of bluish-green and purple and emerald.* Even in slow motion my pictures show the hummingbirds' wings in very rapid beats. How these little birds evolved such bodies with such powerful muscles and such enormous speed of wing motion are additional things which we do not know.

Partly submerged in the brook water were the hard, slightly furry pods and fragments of pods of an almendro tree which grew high over my stone seat.† Troops of white-faced capuchins often plucked these plum-shaped pods. They would scrape off some of the outer plushy coating and eat it, then like some human beings they would discard much good material which was still edible. The monkeys' carelessness in this case was in interesting contrast with the care which they exercised with the nectar-yielding flowers of the balsa tree, but this apparent wastefulness actually served others very well indeed. The discarded pods were first eagerly sought by those rodents, somewhat like overgrown cavies, called agoutis. After a great deal of gnawing, these animals succeeded in cutting through the rocklike outer shells and obtaining the somewhat conical seeds within. Pods which these rodents missed, collared peccaries found and with their powerful jaw muscles and teeth they split these objects lengthwise and the small seeds then fell out of the oval cavities, and an occasional seed lost by the

* *Phaethornis superciliosus cassinii*, *P. longuemareus saturatus,* and *Thalurania furcata venusta.*
† *Macronemum glabrescens.*

peccaries was quickly recovered by the watchful Canal Zone squirrels.* Remembering also that the *Morpho* butterflies and the two shadowlike species described on page 199 and 201 found some nourishment by sucking even the fermenting shells with their long uncoiled tongues, we see that the white-faced monkeys, by throwing down the partly scraped almendro nuts, were actually benefiting a host of other forest inhabitants. In these few observations we have a good clear example of natural conservation, something which went on wherever we looked in these tropical forests. Another, but well-hidden case, concerned tiny caterpillars and the palo santo tree.† When this big tree dropped its thousands of blossoms that resembled little pink shuttlecocks, the spent petals in hundreds of cases were being consumed by the larvae, which had rolled themselves in neat, matching pink tubes. The no longer needed petals were not only supplying food for the caterpillars, but they were bringing them gently to the ground where they could pupate and transform safely into adult moths.

All at once at certain spots in the forest, zephyrs carrying a soft and delicious perfume halted me enchanted in my tracks, and upon looking up, there, often but a few feet overhead along horizontal branches, would be massed fat buds and lovely open white-and-purplish flowers of a gustavia tree, the throats of these blossoms choked with purple stamens.‡ Short-lived like so many blossoms in the tropics, those of this huge-leaved tree nevertheless had time to send its ephemeral messages abroad, and the wonder of that scent stirred something within me which seemed to open up my

* The three mammals mentioned above are the agouti, *Dasyprocta punctata isthmica,* the collared peccary, *Pecari tajacu bangi,* and the Canal Zone squirrel, *Sciurus granatensis marulus.*
† *Triplaris melaenodendron.*
‡ *Gustavia superba.*

vision to a world beyond the forest in which I stood, a luminous place radiating a special sort of beauty. Flower odors for the bees are simply the plant's method of assuring pollination. Could it be that these same odors are also for the purpose of giving *us* such glimpses of perfection?

Contrasting with these serene *superba* trees were stilt palms, indicating with whorls of pipelike supports jutting out at an angle a few feet above the ground their continual struggle to keep their heavy heads toward the sun. Still higher were the barrigón trees,* whose pale cocoa-colored trunks stretched their curious branches high into the open sunlight. Their tapering limbs were gently bowed here, bent slightly there, calmly and artistically as if they might have suddenly frozen thus while mildly exercising. Their terminal twigs were like slender curving fingers and devoid of leaves in the early part of the year, and their quickly spent flowers were like big white powder puffs when seen high in natural *situ*. Morning after morning for several weeks, from a dozen to a score or more of these three-inch bunches of slender white stamens, apparently in splendid youth, would be seen near the tips of the branches, only to fall one at a time, suddenly, until a little later in the morning all would be lying dead upon the forest floor. I wondered what pollinated them in time, and what was the purpose of this ruthless beheading almost as they came into full blossom.

In this short chapter we can but scratch the surface concerning the organisms which collectively make up the intricate, complex pattern of Barro Colorado Island. The longer we stayed and the more we examined things there, the more intricate the over-all interrelationships seemed. How did all of these organisms of the past and the present fit in with one another? How long had all of this living stuff been there; how long prior to the time when these forested hills became

* *Bombax barrigón.*

forested islands? Doubtless the origin of much of it dated back hundreds of thousands, even millions of years in the case of some of the ants, and antedating all of these things perhaps, the sea must have washed a shore just below where we were studying, for here on a tiny island but a few minutes' paddle from our boat landing I found an amazing exposed deposit of minute marine fossils called Foraminefera, sixteen species of them at least, representatives of a group in which there are thousands of named species, among which are about thirty surface-living ones still in existence.[5] Those which I found as fossil shells or tests looked like minute bits of fluted columns, domes and lintels, or coiled flat objects, or flattened disks, faceted or reticulated with hundreds of slight indentations, this last described species belonging to the genus *Lepidocyclina.*[6]

These are very strange little animals when alive. Within the tests there is apparently little but a jellylike mass containing a nucleus. This substance, like that of an amoeba, may send forth projections or pseudopodia in any direction, but what is so astonishing is the fact that the whole thing sometimes leaves its test and *travels free* as a naked vulnerable mass of living matter. If a tiny piece of this now becomes severed from the main "body," both the original mass and the fragment will proceed to send out streamers toward each other which will eventually meet, coalesce and become one again.[7] No one can explain how cells thus know where they are, or how protoplasm knows in which direction to extend itself in order to succeed in such a union. Here is one of the great mysteries whose solution is wrapped deeply within the formula of life.

I found hundreds of other interesting insects also on this island which should be written up some day—variously camouflaged ones, as well as wonderfully camouflaged frogs and toads which were so perfectly matched with dead leaves or bark or lichens that the animals did not bother to move when confronted, evidently instinctively realizing their safety. Astonishing as it may seem, here were also some of the same microscopic animals which I found at home in Connecticut, some of the one-celled ones seemed to be even the same species. One rotifer which looked exactly like the *citrinus,* described as being so common at home, also appeared in these Panama cultures produced from dry, sun-baked weeds which had been lying in the clearing.

Wonderful, and sometimes mysterious sounds issued from the forest in the direction of the brooklet at night. Hauntingly at evening, and again perhaps at long intervals during the nights, came the sad but sweet voice of the great tinamou.* The first ascending tremolo whistles came as the short dusk was fading. This voice was one of the most compelling yet cryptic sounds from the forest blackness. Often I would stop upon hearing it to try to imagine what was actually going on within my head when these pleasing notes or any other strange forest sounds came to me. Were the sweet sad notes of this bird nothing more than air disturbances entering the horns which were my ears, striking my tympani and being somehow carried on by my "hammers" and "anvils" and "stirrups" (ossicles) to my middle ears, and thence to my lymph-filled inner ears, and from these cochleae to my "Organs of Corti," and thence to tremendously sensitive minute hair cells, the final auditory receptors? I wonder. Even if anatomists *know* what happens to sound waves when they reach us, no one can yet say how a human being plucks these vibrations out of the atmosphere and converts them into messages which contact us at once with the joys of aesthetic sensation and experience.

What makes the tinamou's voice sad and sweet in my brain? What happens when the oropéndolas's gurgles and

* *Tinamus major castaneiceps.*

those of the brooklet strike the same chords within me? These are the sort of questions whose answers we cannot begin to form satisfactorily. In them we find the deep pleasures of which only man may be conscious and so again set him apart from all the rest of the primates.

Other strange sounds at night came no doubt from tree frogs, but there were still other much weirder ones whose sources we could not even guess. They came in two vocal levels, both soft and mysterious, one pitched slightly below the other, like two tympani in an orchestra. Whenever the first creature called, the other would immediately answer, and this odd duet might continue on and on for hours at a stretch with only short intermissions. I cannot describe these voices adequately, voices so strange and so muffled, as though they might have issued from some unnamed animals in a state of near exhaustion. Many people at the island never heard them at all and I am glad that I have my tape records to prove that I did. Often in the night I would get up just to listen, to record them and to try to imagine what these creatures were like which uttered them. I do not believe in trying to write down such things as a rule, but most people who read this book will never have the opportunity to hear either the records, or the voices themselves in their natural surroundings, so I will venture to do so this time. To my ears the first voice seemed to say "ub-ub-ub-ub," followed almost at once by the other one answering "wub-wub-wub-wub." By repeating the syllables of the first voice in an extremely low and quiet tone, and then answering yourself by repeating the second group of syllables in a still deeper, still softer tone, you may receive at least a suggestion of how these enigmas of the forest communicated to each other. I would dearly love to know what they were.

We left the forested island with a thousand memories and probably as many unanswered questions. What had caused the growth of those enormous top-heavy beaks of the toucans which always seemed to pull them down in flight? Why did the slaty antshrike * make its transparent nest always of jet-black tendrils which looked for all the world like tangled horsehair? And why did these birds always choose this baffling material which we could never discover *growing* anywhere in the forest ourselves during nine weeks of searching? I found nine nests of this antshrike, but only one contained a little green moss in addition to that standard material, whatever it may consist of.

What strange urges played through the tiny brains of the red-capped manakins,† periodically causing these little black, scarlet-headed, yellow-thighed and china-white-eyed birds to come shrieking and darting through the forest like living bullets, to land upon long chosen, long used, even polished perches, and there to glide backward or forward upon tiny feet which moved so rapidly that the individual steps blended into smooth uninterrupted performances as though the manakins were traveling upon tiny invisible dollies? What caused them at other times to sit almost motionless for long, patience-trying periods doing absolutely nothing except uttering an occasional weak call, then suddenly to hop madly from one perch to another several times, to repeat, turning in an instant from facing in one direction to facing in the opposite direction, and to flip their wings so rapidly and with such great energy that loud sounds came forth which I likened to the crackling of large electric sparks? Not far away, other male birds in their chosen territories invariably took up this buzzing and snapping in response to the first one to start the weird periodic procedure, which went on day in, day out during all of the weeks which we spent on Barro Colorado. Was this entirely a courtship com-

* *Thamnophilus punctatus atrinucha.*
† *Pipra mentalis minor.*

plex, I wondered? Not once did a bird of the opposite sex make herself visible during all of my observations while I was making motion pictures of the dances of the males, so I cannot supply the answer.

I wondered why snakes were so seldom encountered on an island where they must have been numerous. In nine weeks I saw eight. One was a brilliant-green tree snake which came down a vine beside me. All the others, in every case observed along the trails, made off into the forest with such haste that I could not even describe their patterns.

And there was the sloth, discovered one early morning curled up and fast asleep upon its back fifteen feet above the forest floor at the junction of two crossing vines. A little later and farther along the same trail, my wife picked up the big, freshly eaten-out shell of an armadillo just where it had been left during the night by some large predator. Things about these mammals set us wondering again. How did that algal species which grows only upon the hair of the sloth find this niche in the first place? How did the armadillo grow those protective shell sections, evolved like bands of man-made armor? And those wild peccaries which we once met on the trail, and at another time at really close quarters as I was photographing the dance of the red-capped manakins, why did they turn and run ignominiously, after all we had heard to the contrary? Every day we found ourselves asking why and how, again and again, but seldom were the answers forthcoming.

Anyone who studies anatomy is astonished by the truly bewildering number of things which there are to remember, or to try to remember, by name. Not only are there these thousands of named parts of living things, but equally numerous functions and processes which we know are carried out by organs, or various parts of organs, even in the smallest bodies. In dealing with such creatures as mammals and birds, these functions and processes seem staggering in number and complexity, but right on down through the phyla it is the same story everywhere. Down through the serpents and geckos and iguanas of this island, down through its huge toads and its tiny frogs; the diminutive fishes of the brooklet, its snails and worms, its myriad insects and other arthropods, even in its hidden micro-organisms of the water and vegetation. The more we examine and study them, the more complicated all questions concerning them become.

Now stop for a minute to consider the successful whole which we have observed here on Barro Colorado even from a *single anatomical angle*. What, for instance, has made possible the endless variations of a digestive system: all of the necessary solvents and chemical combinations, the myriad enzymes whose chemical chains are so complex that they may never be fully analyzed, and the thousands of actions, interactions, and reactions within all of these living creatures which make it possible for each one of them to eat and digest and *enjoy* their food, to dissolve and sift, to retain the good, and to re-employ endless kinds of fuel without a single thought of how, and so to dispose of their greatly altered body wastes that the world of plants may also be benefited and continue to grow along with them as the basic reservoir?

What has brought eyes of one sort or another to each and every normally visible creature here, from the compound eyes of the tiniest insects to the exquisite ones of birds, and our own wonderful optical instruments which may see not only all of these things of the forest, but which are also capable of peering through millions of light years of space to the stars and the nebula of Andromeda without the aid of a telescope? These are but two more of the endless unanswered questions which make life for man so exciting.

Does the *individual* cell hold all of the secrets which we

great aggregates of them cannot fathom even with the massed myriads which make up our brains? I prefer to believe that there is an unfathomable profile, built of something else again, which comprehends and gives impetus to cells and atoms and all of their accomplishments, and controls them with the ease with which *we* comprehend a and b and c.

And now as I come to the final paragraph, the rain of spring is pouring down upon the greenery in a once more unfolding world. Looking out of my study windows, I see the big drops tapping and bobbing the fresh emerald foliage, and I know that now such tiny entities as the colpidiums, which we have come to know so well, are once more finding release from inaction, perhaps release from guard-cell prisons among the wetted leaves. Like all of the other living things, they are, even though unconsciously in this case, responding at the proper instant to the medicine of God.

Documentation and
Reference Notes

CHAPTER 1

1. Huxley, Julian. *What Is Science?* (New York: Simon and Schuster, 1955), p. 279.

2. *Ibid.*, p. 279.

3. Allee, Warder Clyde. *What is Science?* (New York: Simon and Schuster, 1955), pp. 249-50.

4. Cuénot, Lucien, with collaboration of Tétry, Andrée. *L'Evolution Biologique, les Faits, les Incertitudes* (Paris: Masson & Cie., 1951). See *Quarterly Review of Biology*, Vol. 29, No. 4, p. 354.

5. Beadle, George. *Scientific American Reader* (New York: Simon and Schuster, 1955), p. 278.

6. Wald, George. *The Physics and Chemistry of Life* (New York: Simon and Schuster, 1957), p. 9.

7. Villee, Claude A. *Biology* (Philadelphia and London: W. B. Saunders Company, 2nd Edition, 1955), p. 130.

8. *Ibid.*, p. 546. See also Scrader, Franz. *The Movement of Chromosomes in Cell Division* (New York: Columbia University Press, 1st and 2nd Editions, 1953). Also *Quarterly Review of Biology*, Vol. 29, No. 1, March, 1954, p. 60.

9. *Ibid.*, p. 240.

10. *Ibid.*, pp. 557, 559.

11. Sinnott, Edmund W. *Biology of the Spirit* (New York: The Viking Press, 1955), p. 57.

12. Gray, George W. *The New Astronomy* (New York: Simon and Schuster, 1957), p. 45.

13. Kahn, Fritz. *Design of the Universe* (New York: Crown Publishers, 1954), Part III, Chapter III.

14. Payne-Gaposchkin, Cecilia. *The New Astronomy* (New York: Simon and Schuster, 1957), p. 107.

15. Alfvén, Hannes. *The New Astronomy* (New York: Simon and Schuster, 1957), pp. 74, 75.

16. Zacharias, Jerrold R. *New York Times* report on symposium of the American Association for the Advancement of Science, December 28, 1956.

CHAPTER 2

1. Villee, Claude A. *Biology* (Philadelphia and London: W. B. Saunders Company, 1955), p. 483.
2. Sinnott, Edmund W. *Biology of the Spirit* (New York: The Viking Press, 1955), p. 102.
3. Villee, Claude A. *Biology* (Philadelphia and London: W. B. Saunders Company, 1955), p. 453.
4. Simpson, George Gaylord. *The Meaning of Evolution* (New Haven: The Yale University Press, 1952), p. 216.
5. Spoerl, Edward. *Atomic Power* (New York: Simon and Schuster, 1957), pp. 139, 140.
6. Villee, Claude A. *Biology* (Philadephia and London: W. B. Saunders Company, 1955), pp. 465, 466, 467, 478.

CHAPTER 4

1. Kudo, Richard Ruksabro. *Handbook of Protozoology* (Springfield, Illinois, and Baltimore: Charles C. Thomas, 1931), p. 8.
2. Du Nöuy, Lecomte. *Human Destiny* (New York: Longmans, Green and Company, 1947), p. 179.

CHAPTER 5

1. Folsom, J. M. *Nearctic Collembola or Springtails of the Family Iso-tomidae* (Washington: United States National Museum, Bulletin No. 168, May, 1937), p. 111.
2. *Ibid.*, p. 74.
3. Rowher, S. A. *Journal of the Washington Academy of Sciences,* Vol. 13, No. 16, October, 1923.
4. Jeans, J. H. *The Mysterious Universe* (Cambridge: The University Press, 1930), p. 158.

CHAPTER 6

1. McKinley, G. Murray. *Evolution: The Ages and Tomorrow* (New York: The Ronald Press Company, 1956), p. 153.
2. Darwin, Charles. *Different Forms of Flowers on Plants of the Same Species* (New York: D. Appleton and Company, 1893), Chapter IV, on heterostyled trimorphic plants.
3. Villee, Claude A. *Biology* (Philadelphia and London: W. B. Saunders Company, 1955), p. 396. In reference to sensory cells of smell: "They occur singly (in nasal cavity) and are distinguished from ordinary epithelial cells by hairs which project into the mucous layer."

CHAPTER 7

1. Hartshorne, Charles. *Monotony-Threshold in Singing Birds* (Lancaster, Pennsylvania: *The Auk,* Organ of the American Ornithologists' Union, 1956), Vol. 73, No. 2, April, 1956, pp. 176-92.

CHAPTER 8

1. Berrill, N. J. *Sex and the Nature of Things* (New York: Dodd, Mead and Company, 1953), p. 96.
2. Villee, Claude A. *Biology* (Philadelphia and London: W. B. Saunders Company, 1955), pp. 29, 30.

CHAPTER 9

1. Miner, Roy Waldo. *Field Book of Seashore Life* (New York: G. P. Putnam's Sons, 1955), p. 486.

CHAPTER 10

1. Hodge, W. H. Economic Botanist, United States Department of Agriculture Research Administration, Division of Plant Exploration and Introduction, author of *The Flora of Dominica, B. W. I.* "I was glad to receive the information concerning the ascent of Mt. Diablotin and I judge that insofar as I know, you are the only person to have climbed to the top. I was able to get only three-fourths of the way to the summit." Whether or not any person has been up there since my expedition is unknown to the author of this book.
2. Barbour, Thomas. *Reptiles and Amphibians* (Boston and New York: Houghton, Mifflin Company, 1926), p. 95. Barbour supposed this frog to be very deadly, which was proved untrue.
3. Breland, Osmond P. *Harmless or Deadly?,* The American Museum of Natural History's magazine, *Natural History,* Vol. LXII, No. 9, November, 1953, p. 406.
4. Bogert, Charles M. *Useful Drugs from Toads?, Natural History Magazine,* Vol. LXIII, No. 10, December, 1954, p. 470. The big toads of Panama which *are* poisonous are described.
5. Emiliana, Cesare. *Sea Frontiers* (Coral Gables Marine Laboratory of the University of Miami, 1958), Vol. 4, No. 1, February, 1958. This is the Bulletin of the International Oceanographic Foundation. "More than 50,000 species of Foraminifera have been identified, including around 30 species of surface-living ones existing now."
6. Cooper, G. Arthur. Head Curator of the Department of Geology, Smithsonian Institution, U. S. National Museum, writes under date of March 18, 1957: "The specimens sent for examination and report have been

examined by Mr. Raymond Douglass, U. S. Geological Survey, who reports: 'The rounded objects are a kind of Foraminifera called *Lepidocyclina.*' Specimens similar to yours were described and illustrated by W. Storrs Cole, U. S. Geological Survey Professional Paper 244. Some of the specimens described are from Barro Colorado. A summary of the geology of Barro Colorado Island, by W. P. Woodring, is being processed for publication by the Smithsonian Institution."

Specimens of *L. miraflorensis* were collected one-half mile south of Miraflores Station, Panama Canal Zone (U. S. Geological Survey locality No. 6255) around 1927 by Dr. D. F. MacDonald. "The horizon is supposed to be the lower Miocene, Emperador Limestone, but the stratigraphic position is not definitely known." The above notes are important in view of the finding of these specimens by the author at Slothia, the little island referred to in the text. See *Proceedings of the U. S. National Museum,* Vol. 71, art. 8, p. 4.

7. Cushman, Joseph Augustine. *Observations on Living Specimens of Iridia diaphana, a species of Foraminifera* (Washington: *Proceedings of the U. S. National Museum,* 1920), Vol. 57, pp. 153-58.

Index

Technical Index to Organisms